SHERMAN TANK

1941 onwards (all M4 variants)

First published in April 2012
Reprinted in October 2017

A catalogue record for this book is available from the British Library

ISBN 978 0 85733 101 4

Library of Congress control no. 2011943850

Published by Haynes Publishing,
Sparkford, Yeovil, Somerset BA22 7JJ, UK
Tel: 01963 440635
Int. tel: +44 1963 440635
Website: www.haynes.com

Haynes North America Inc.
859 Lawrence Drive, Newbury Park,
California 91320, USA

Printed in Malaysia

COVER CUTAWAY: *Richard Chasemore*

Contents

'There is many a boy here today who looks on war as all glory, but, boys, it is all hell.'

William Tecumseh Sherman, 1820–91

Introduction

Fifty years after his death, William Tecumseh Sherman unwittingly lent his name to the US Army's medium tank. From an age of sabre-wielding cavalrymen, Sherman certainly could not have visualised a conflict in which massive armoured vehicles would duel one another with guns of unimaginable destructive power. Yet the choice of Sherman's name seems as appropriate for one of the most iconic fighting vehicles of all time, as do the words that he used to address the graduating class of the Michigan Military Academy in 1879. War is, indeed, hell.

OPPOSITE The length of the Chrysler 30-cylinder multi-bank engine necessitated extending the hull of the M4A4, which resulted in the bogies being spaced further apart. All M4A4s had the three-piece bolted differential housing. *(Ian Young)*

Whilst the German Tiger is almost certainly the best-known tank of World War Two, albeit its reputation far exceeds its real achievements, it is the Allied M4 Sherman medium tank that deserves our admiration and respect, if only for the bravery of its crews when faced with the superiority of the later German machines. Indeed, when compared directly with the German tanks the Sherman was really no better than adequate... leading one Sherman crewman to wonder whether anyone involved in its design had actually been required to fight in it!

It would certainly be true to say that the Sherman lacked sophistication, but, of course, things are never that straightforward, and it did

at least have the advantage of being simple to build, reliable, and easy to drive. Constructed in large numbers between 1941 and 1945, the Sherman served with the US Army and Marine Corps, the British Army, the British Commonwealth Armies, the Soviet Union, the Free French, the Polish government-in-exile, and the armies of Brazil and China, during World War Two. It also remained in service some three or more decades beyond the end of the war, notably seeing service with both sides during the war between India and Pakistan in 1965, and during the Israeli Defence Force's struggles with its neighbours during the Six-Day War in 1967 and the Yom Kippur War in 1973.

The Sherman's most serious drawback was the main gun, which was never better than the German guns and which, as the war progressed, became increasingly outclassed. With the original 75mm M3 gun the Sherman could not defeat either a Panther or a Tiger on equal terms and, even after the 75mm weapon was replaced by the 76mm M1 anti-tank gun in 1944 there was little chance of defeating a

Panther or a Tiger unless it could be hit from the side or the rear, where the armour was thinner. However, the more powerful German guns could always penetrate the Sherman's frontal armour, and it wasn't until the British 17-pounder (76.2mm) gun was used to create the Sherman Firefly in 1943/44, that the M4 finally became a match for the heavier

ABOVE M4A4 of the British 2nd Army photographed in Bremen in April 1945. Note the *appliqué* armour on the hull sides and the spare bogie wheels and track sections carried on the nose. *(Tank Museum)*

LEFT Rear view of a US Army M4 that has been fitted with wading ducts in preparation for an amphibious assault. Note how the official censor has removed a part of the picture to the upper right, presumably to prevent the location being identified. *(Tank Museum)*

German tanks, even if the larger gun did make for cramped conditions in the fighting compartment.

Tanks are generally measured by three criteria – firepower, manoeuvrability and protection – and if the Sherman fell short in each of these areas when compared to the German machines, it did at least score on its sheer ubiquity. Total Sherman production over a four-year period amounted to slightly fewer than 49,500 units, whilst an American tank industry report put total German gun-tank production for the years 1940 to 1945 at just 24,360, of which 1,368 were the feared Tiger I and just 569 were the Tiger II or *Königstiger*.

LEFT Late model cast-hull M4A1 with the distinctive *appliqué* armour that was used to protect the ammunition stowage areas. *(Tank Museum)*

BELOW Seen outside the US Army Armor Centre at Fort Knox in 1990, this M4A3 with the improved horizontal volute spring suspension system mounts a 76mm gun fitted with a muzzle brake. A completely new turret design was required to house the larger gun. *(Specialist Torrey A. Mapp, US Army)*

'The armored division is a powerfully armed and armored, highly mobile force. Its outstanding characteristics are its battlefield mobility and its protected firepower.'

US Army Field Manual, FM 100:1941, Operations

The Sherman story

The M4 Sherman tank was a direct development of the M3, which had seen its first action with the British Army in North Africa in May 1942. By that time the M3 was already being superseded by the much improved M4, with the latter continuing in production to the end of the conflict. Although lacking the sophistication of German tanks, the Sherman was reliable, manoeuvrable, easy to drive and, above all, it was easy to produce... what it lacked in firepower and protection, it more than made up for in availability.

OPPOSITE The M4A1 cast-hull variant was the first Sherman to enter production. The first production example was retained by the US Army, whilst the second came to Britain. Although it was eventually re-gunned with the later 75mm M3 weapon, in this photograph 'Michael' retains the early M2 short-barrel gun with its distinctive counterweight, and is still fitted with a pair of bow machine guns in a fixed mount in the hull; these were deleted from later production. *(Tank Museum)*

Although there had been experiments with armoured traction engines and ammunition trains during the South African or Anglo-Boer War (1899–1902), the modern armoured fighting vehicle is scarcely 100 years old. Early attempts at designing what could be considered a tank had appeared in France, and subsequently in Austria before World War One, but it was the British who came up with the first practical armoured fighting vehicle (AFV) in an attempt to break the stalemate on the Western Front. British tanks saw their first action in 1916, but by the end of the conflict similar machines were in service with the armies of Britain, France, Germany, Italy and the USA.

There are many who would argue that, lacking a proper understanding as to how this new and terrifying weapon should be deployed, the British threw away any potential tactical advantage that might have been gained from the first use of the tank. It was to be a further two decades before the tactics of fighting with tanks came to be properly understood, but the German campaigns in the months leading up to World War Two showed what tanks and infantry could achieve under well-trained commanders who understood their strengths and weaknesses. During the so-called *Blitzkrieg* attacks on Poland, the Netherlands and France, the *Wehrmacht* quickly showed themselves to be the masters of tank warfare, utilising fast-moving columns of tanks alongside highly-trained infantry, and even paratroops.

The development of the tank

Experiments into the feasibility of producing ironclad 'landships' had started at the end of the 19th century, when Winston Churchill, as First Lord of the Admiralty, established what was known as the 'Landship Committee'. The Committee was asked to investigate the possibility of developing a cross-country armoured vehicle that could mount a large-calibre gun, and which, at the same time, would be sufficiently well protected to be able to operate under fire on the battlefield. Lieutenant Colonel Ernest D. Swinton drew up the first specification for such a machine in October 1914, but initial experiments, using wheeled vehicles, were

disappointing. However, the continuous caterpillar crawler track that had been devised by the American Benjamin Holt in 1907 seemed to suggest that there was a way forward.

In September 1915 William Foster & Co, an agricultural engineering company based in Lincoln, constructed 'Little Willie', the first practical tracked armoured vehicle, designed by William Tritton and Lieutenant Walter G. Wilson. Within the space of a few months 'Little Willie' was followed by a second prototype, dubbed 'Mother' or 'Big Willie', which was sufficiently successful that Fosters were contracted to build an initial 25 units, with the Metropolitan Amalgamated Railway Carriage & Wagon Company making a contribution towards a further 150. Described as 'tank, Mk I', these early vehicles were constructed from riveted boilerplate and consisted of a rhomboidal box-like hull with unsprung linked steel tracks wrapped around the perimeter. Initially two versions were produced: the so-called 'males' were equipped with 6-pounder (57mm) guns, whilst the females were armed only with machine guns. For reasons of security, the machines were initially described as 'water carriers for Mesopotamia' – thus giving rise to the name 'tank'. By 1917 the Mk VIII tank was being constructed to a standardised design in Britain and the USA.

At the beginning of 1917 – realising, perhaps, that there was scope for a lighter, faster machine – the War Office drew up a specification for a smaller 'medium tank'. The first of these was the twin-engined medium Mk A or Whippet, designed by William Tritton and William Rigby, which saw its first action in March 1918. Next came the Mk B, incorporating elements of the original Mk I and the Whippet, and designed by Walter G. Wilson, who by now was a major. This was followed by the Mk C, or Hornet, of 1917, of which some 200 examples were constructed.

The Germans were quick to copy the British invention, and the first production example of their huge *Stürmpanzerwagen A7V* was ready by October 1917. This was followed by the *Leicht Kampfwagen* (Lk II) in 1918, which was effectively a copy of a captured Whippet. The first French tanks, in the form of the Schneider *Char d'Assaut 1* (CA 1) and the

Char St Chamond, had also appeared in 1916, and the most significant French tank design of World War One, the Renault *Char Canon FT-17 automitrailleuse à chenilles*, of 1917 was the first tank to incorporate a revolving turret. This design was also adopted by the US Army as the M1917.

Tank production in Britain more or less came to a halt after the Armistice was signed in November 1918. Although many of the existing heavy and medium tanks remained in service, the development of new tank designs during the interwar years was hampered by the political climate – which shied away from even considering the possibility of another major conflict – and by a lack of funds. Most of the British tanks produced during these years were far from satisfactory, generally being underpowered and lacking sufficient firepower and protection. The situation in the USA was similar.

In Germany tank design advanced – covertly – in leaps and bounds, with the first post-war prototypes appearing as early as 1927, when Daimler-Benz, Rheinmetall and Krupps were each asked to construct two experimental tanks, described as *Grossentraktoren*. Krupps and Rheinmetall were subsequently asked to produce two lighter machines described as *Leichttraktoren*. These were followed by a medium tank and, in 1933, Krupps eventually received a contract to build 135 armoured vehicles, described under the code name *Landwirtschaftlicher Schlepper* (*LaS*) and passed off as agricultural machines.

By 1933 the LaS had developed into the *Panzerkampfwagen I* (*PzKpfw I*), a light tank armed with a pair of 7.92mm machine guns; it was also constructed without a turret as a training vehicle. During the Spanish Civil War it became obvious that the *PzKpfw I* was too lightly armed to be effective and that it was also underpowered, leading to the use of a more powerful engine in the *PzKpfw IB* variant. Production ended in 1937, although it had been replaced by the *PzKpfw II* a year earlier. The 7.92mm machine guns were replaced by a 20mm cannon which provided a degree of anti-tank capability, but much more significant were the heavier *PzKpfw III* and *PzKpfw IV* tanks that first appeared in 1936 and 1937 respectively. Whilst the former was armed with a 37mm gun,

the latter mounted a distinctive short-barrelled 75mm gun, but both were designed to allow subsequent improvements in firepower, the *PzKpfw III* acquiring a 50mm gun in 1940 and ending its career with a 75mm weapon, the *PzKpfw IV* eventually acquiring a long-barrelled 75mm gun.

It would be fair to say that by 1939 German tank design represented the state of the art in mechanised warfare. Throughout World War Two improvements in both firepower and protection generally kept the German tanks one step ahead, and the German heavy tanks – the Panther (*PzKpfw V*) and the much-feared Tiger (*PzKpfw VI*) entered service in 1943 and 1941 respectively, the *PzKpfw VI Ausf* E production variant of the latter mounting the formidable 88mm anti-tank gun, a weapon that struck fear into the hearts of Allied tank crews.

For most of the war years the Allied tanks were no match for these mighty German machines in any respect, and the Sherman, which was introduced in 1941, was no exception. Although the Allies were well aware of its shortcomings there was no question of designing a replacement. In an attempt to improve its firepower, in 1944 the 75mm main gun was replaced by the 76mm M1 anti-

BELOW Despite the numbers produced, the M4 Sherman was never really more than a stopgap design and was based largely on the lower hull and automotive arrangements of the M3 Lee/Grant medium tank. *(US DoD)*

tank gun. This offered some improvements in performance, but not of a sufficient order of magnitude and, in a stand-off, the more-powerful German guns could still penetrate the Sherman's frontal armour, whilst the Sherman had little chance of defeating a Panther or a Tiger unless it could shoot it from the side or the rear, where the armour was thinner. In truth there were only two Allied tanks which could engage with a Tiger or Panther on a more or less equal basis – the British Comet, a cruiser tank which was equipped with a 77mm gun, and the Sherman Firefly, a British conversion which saw the standard 76mm M1 gun of the Sherman replaced by a British 17-pounder (76.2mm).

That the Allied tanks were able to prevail against German armour that was generally better designed, better protected and better armed, probably says more about the skill, courage and determination of the crews, and the sheer number of tanks available on the battlefield, than it does about the design of the machines themselves.

Development of the M4 medium tank

The US Army's M4 medium tank – dubbed the 'General Sherman' by the British, but more commonly known just as the Sherman – was a direct development of the hastily conceived and curiously turreted M3 of 1941. This, in turn, had been rushed into development in 1940 when it became obvious that the M2A1 medium tank, which was armed with nothing more lethal than a 37mm main gun, would be no match for the German *PzKpfw III* and *PzKpfw IV*. Unfortunately the hull of the M2 was not able to accommodate a larger turret ring and it was decided, purely as an interim measure, to mount a 75mm howitzer in a side sponson. The result was initially known as the medium tank T5E2.

Although the sponson-mounting meant that the gun had a very limited traverse, which often led to the tank having to be manoeuvred into position for firing rather than simply rotating and elevating the turret, the gun was at least a match for the then-current German tanks. On 28 August 1941 the contract that had been placed with Chrysler in August the previous year

for the construction of 1,000 examples of the M2A1 in a new government-financed, purpose-built tank arsenal in Detroit, was cancelled. Meanwhile, Rock Island Arsenal completed the construction of less than 100 examples of their planned 126 M2A1 medium tanks and, at the same time, started the detailed design work necessary to turn the prototype T5E2 into the production M3.

Rock Island Arsenal's engineers spent just 60 days on the design work for the M3, which meant that there was little opportunity for any radical rethinking. The basic hull and the Wright (or Continental) air-cooled radial engine and running gear of the M2A1 were retained, as was the vertical volute spring suspension (VVSS). As with the T5E2 prototype, a 75mm gun was fitted into a sponson on the right-hand side of the hull, with the traverse limited to 15° either side of the centreline. With a nod to its artillery origins, the gun was expected to be able to fire 5,000–7,500 rounds before the barrel was sufficiently worn to require replacement; this subsequently proved to be wishful thinking, with few tanks surviving in the field long enough to fire even 5,000 rounds. A 37mm M5 or M6 gun was mounted in a small revolving turret on the left-hand side of the hull and, on top of this, there was what appeared to be a second, smaller, turret mounting a 0.30in machine gun, but which was actually a commander's cupola.

It was clear that Rock Island Arsenal lacked the facilities to produce the numbers of tanks that would be required, and under the auspices of the Tank Committee manufacturing was out-sourced to the American automotive and locomotive industries. Production started in April 1941, with an initial 1,000 tanks intended for the US Army. The British Purchasing Committee placed orders for a further 1,686 examples on a strict 'cash and carry' basis, but being unhappy with some features of the design the British version mounted a larger cast turret, lacking the cupola but redesigned to accommodate a Number 19 radio set in a bustle. The British Army described 'their' version as the M3 General Grant, whilst the US Army version was the M3 General Lee, although the word General was soon dropped.

Although it was never intended as anything other than an interim design, some 6,258

examples were constructed between April 1941 and November 1942. The type saw service with the British and US Armies during the early years of World War Two, and was finally declared obsolete in April 1944.

Even before the specification for the M3 was finalised, the US Armored Force Board had started to try to nail down the requirements for its successor, at first described as the T6 medium tank but subsequently to become known as the M4 medium tank. Writing in the official history of British wartime production in 1952, the historian M.M. Postan claimed that the Canadian-built Ram tank, which was based on the American M3 medium design, influenced the United States project for the M4 Sherman. There are also suggestions that informal discussions with the British Tank Board may well have helped to shape the final specification, since by this time the British had the benefit of two years' experience of fighting the panzers of the German Army.

However, regardless of how much it may have differed from the M3, the M4 was essentially a child of the same parents. It retained the lower hull of the earlier machine, together with the Continental or Wright R-975-C1 engine, the transmission, and the running gear, but with sufficient space to fit a larger engine should one become available subsequently. The design of the upper hull was completely new, and the proposals included both cast and welded forms of construction, mounting a new fully-traversing powered turret of cast construction, which was designed to make it easy to fit alternative weapons to allow the same chassis to be used for a variety of roles. At 108in (2,743mm), the overall height of the vehicle was considerably reduced compared to the 123in (3,125mm) height of the M3, and the number of crew members was reduced to five. The weight was held to around 30 tons – as prescribed by 'US Army Regulation 850-15', which decreed that no tank should weigh more than 30 tons or exceed 103in (2,616mm) in width.

Rock Island Arsenal put forward five different schemes for the M4 in April 1941, differing

LEFT Frontal view of the T6 mock-up showing the three bow machine guns, two in fixed mounts and one in a rotating ball, and the 75mm main gun with a co-axial machine gun alongside the main weapon. *(Tank Museum)*

RIGHT Photographed in September 1941, this is the pilot model T6 produced at Rock Island Arsenal. The main gun is the short-barrelled 75mm M2 weapon and the vehicle retains the four machine guns of the mock-up. *(Tank Museum)*

BELOW The hull of the pilot T6 is of one-piece cast construction and, unlike later production, has a side access door. Note the counterweight fitted to the end of the barrel of the main gun. *(Tank Museum)*

mainly in the choice of weapon – the first mounted a 75mm short-barrelled M2 main gun together with a co-axial machine gun; the second was fitted with a pair of 37mm M6 guns and one machine gun; option three carried a 105mm howitzer together with a single machine gun; the fourth was fitted with three 0.50in anti-aircraft machine guns; whilst the final iteration mounted a British 6-pounder (57mm) gun and a co-axial machine gun.

The Ordnance Committee recommended that a full-size wooden mock-up be produced, and this was completed during the following month for the approval of the Armored Force Board. Two pilot models were then authorised.

The first was constructed at Aberdeen Proving Ground and was completed in September 1941, some six months after the first engineering drawings had been completed. This first example had the distinctively-rounded cast hull, later to become known as the M4A1, and mounted the 75mm gun; unlike production machines, the hull included side doors. The second, which was built by Rock Island Arsenal, had a hull of welded construction, but was never fitted with a turret.

With subsequent modifications, which included the deletion of the hull doors and the commander's cupola, the M4 was approved and standardised in October 1941, with pilot machines constructed during the following month. Production was planned for 11 manufacturing plants, including those already producing the M3, and work started in February 1942 at the Lima Locomotive Works in Lima, Ohio, under British Ministry of Supply (MoS) contract. The first examples to be produced were actually of the cast-hull M4A1 configuration that was known by the British as the Sherman I, and since the M3 75mm gun was not ready for production the first two tanks off the line retained the short-barrelled M2 gun, which necessitated the use of a counterweight at the muzzle. The first of these was retained in the USA for testing purposes, but the second was shipped to Britain and was put

ABOVE Rear view of a production M4A1 showing the engine access doors and the twin air cleaners to either side. *(Tank Museum)*

ABOVE First M4A1 to be produced by Pacific Car & Foundry. Note that the hull access doors have been deleted (in fact they were only fitted to one M4A1, and even then were welded shut), as have the fixed machine guns in the bow. *(Warehouse Collection)*

on display on a plinth in Horse Guards Parade, as the first American-built tank to be delivered to the British Army. Assigned the War Office registration number T25190 (later renumbered T74195), it was named 'Michael', in honour of Michael Dewar, a British industrialist who had led the mission to have tanks constructed in the USA for the British Army. The M2 gun was later replaced by the standard M3 weapon, and in this form 'Michael' has survived to the present day. It is now the oldest Sherman tank still in existence, and can be seen at the Tank Museum in Bovington, Dorset.

The target for the production of the M4 had been 2,000 tanks per month during 1942, and although this figure was not met, by the end of the year Shermans were being constructed at ten plants – American Locomotive, Baldwin Locomotive, Detroit Tank Arsenal, Federal Machine & Welder, Fisher Tank Grand Blanc, Ford Motor Company, Lima Locomotive, Pacific Car & Foundry, the Pressed Steel Car Company, and Pullman-Standard. By the spring of 1943 both light and medium tanks were coming off the production lines at a (combined) rate of about 4,000 vehicles per month, against a theoretical production capacity of 7,705 tanks per month. Curiously, the price per tank varied wildly between plants – at the Chrysler Detroit Tank Arsenal a Sherman cost $42,400, whereas

at Federal Machine & Welder the cost was close to $70,000.

By the time production was in full swing the Sherman had evolved into six major production variants, with the differences mostly confined to the engine and the method of constructing the hull. Never more than a pragmatic solution to producing a tank that could take on the *Wehrmacht*, once the design was standardised unnecessary changes were kept to a minimum.

BELOW Early M4A1 with one-piece cast differential housing and unusual centrally-mounted siren. *(Tank Museum)*

Aside from the change from a 75mm to 76mm gun, and the use of the 17-pounder (76.2mm) gun in the British Sherman Firefly, the most notable change was to the suspension, with the original vertical volute spring design giving way to a more effective horizontal configuration. Other minor changes included the addition of a powered ventilator in the turret roof, a roof hatch for the assistant driver, and shields to exclude bullet splash, including a rotor shield to the gun mount; the armoured protection for the engine air intake was also improved, and US Army tanks incorporated a mount for an anti-aircraft gun on the turret.

The Sherman saw its first action with the 8th Army at El Alamein in October 1942, where 150 M4A1s fought with three British regiments alongside British-built machines. The Shermans proved themselves to be reliable, easy to operate and, with a so-called dual-purpose gun which allowed both high-explosive and armour-piercing ammunition to be fired, were also considered to be more versatile than the home-grown tanks.

ABOVE Shermans saw their first action with the British 8th Army at El Alamein in October 1942, where 150 M4A1s fought with three British Regiments alongside British-built machines. The official caption to this photograph describes the M4A1 as 'one of the new Sherman tanks'. *(IWM, E17899)*

RIGHT Brand new sand-coloured Sherman being off-loaded from a flat-bed railcar in Egypt in July 1943. *(Tank Museum)*

RIGHT Some development work on the Sherman continued into the post-war years, and in a quest for more effective secondary armaments the commander's cupola of this 106mm gun equipped M4A3 has been replaced by a T121 twin machine-gun mount carrying a pair of 0.30in Brownings. Although trials of the installation were conducted between April 1946 and May 1947, it was eventually deemed unsatisfactory. *(Tank Museum)*

RIGHT The M4A5 Grizzly used the basic hull and automotive arrangements of the cast-hull M4A1, but was built at the Canadian Montreal Locomotive Works. Major differences included a thicker hull (75mm rather than 51mm) and a 17-tooth drive sprocket to suit the shorter-pitch Canadian dry-pin (CDP) tracks. *(Phil Royal)*

BELOW Seen at the Tank Museum's Tankfest show, this M4A3 Sherman has the long 76mm gun and HVSS suspension, which necessitated the use of wider tracks. *(Simon Thomson)*

ABOVE Privately-owned M4A1 equipped with the 76mm M1 gun showing the improved turret with its integral counterweight. Note the pistol port in the turret side. *(Phil Royal)*

ABOVE RIGHT Photographed 'somewhere in England' in mid-1944, this line-up of Shermans shows the *appliqué* armour that was applied to the right-hand face of the turret, where the armour had been reduced in thickness to accommodate the powered traverse gear. The fitters are checking the waterproofing. *(Tank Museum)*

RIGHT Rear view of the M4A5 Grizzly. *(Warehouse Collection)*

LEFT M4A4 with *appliqué* armour; the purpose of the strips applied to the length of the hull is not known. *(Tank Museum)*

BELOW The versatility and mechanical reliability of the Sherman hull meant that it was widely adopted as the basis for a range of other armoured vehicles even after the end of World War Two. Based on the wide-track M4A3, this is the M74 tank recovery vehicle, which replaced the similar M32 in the post-war years. Over 1,000 examples were produced during 1954–55 by Bowen-McLaughlin-York, with others converted from redundant M32s. *(Roy Stephenson)*

The most far-reaching change in production plans for medium tanks in 1942 was the shift from the Grant (M3) to the Sherman (M4).

US Army in World War II: the Ordnance Department: procurement and supply

Chapter Two

Sherman variants

⊏━━━(●)━━━━━━━━━━━━━━━━━⊐

As the M3 medium tank had been adapted for other roles, so too was the Sherman. By the time production ceased in 1945 it had been produced in six main variants – as a gun tank it mounted four different main guns, but it was also adapted as a self-propelled gun, mine-clearance vehicle, armoured recovery vehicle, bridgelayer, rocket-launcher, armoured personnel carrier and flame-thrower. In its many incarnations the Sherman was the most significant element of the Allied tank force throughout World War Two.

OPPOSITE Privately-owned cast-hull M4A1 Sherman IIC Firefly, with the British 17-pounder (76.2mm) gun being put through its paces. The Firefly was the only Sherman variant with any chance of defeating the heavier German tanks at a similar range. *(Simon Thomson)*

volute spring suspension (HVSS) are apparent in the appearance of the vehicle, other modifications – such as the use of *appliqué* armour or the adoption of wet ammunition storage – are less obvious.

Shermans also remained in widespread use around the world in the three or four decades following World War Two, seeing plenty of action, and, not surprisingly, development continued during this period. As the tanks began to show their age in terms of automotive performance or firepower, many were upgraded with new engines, transmission and main gun. Most notable of these are the so-called Israeli M51 'Super Shermans'.

Gun tank variants

There are seven major variants of the M4 Sherman, differing largely in the method of construction of the hull, and the choice of power unit. However, the tank was constantly reviewed, often more to expedite production than improve the breed; changes were made throughout the production run, and the number of detail differences from one tank to another make the situation appear infinitely more complex. Whilst changes such as the replacement of the original 75mm gun with a 76mm weapon and the adoption of horizontal

M4

Production of the base model M4 – Sherman I, to the British Army – was started at the Pressed Steel Car Company in July 1942, and this variant was subsequently also produced by American Locomotive, Baldwin Locomotive, Detroit Tank Arsenal and Pullman-Standard.

The upper hull was of welded construction, while the cast turret was identical to that fitted to the M4A1, which had actually been first into production. It was believed that the welded construction would speed the manufacturing process and reduce bottlenecks, but it had the added bonus of allowing maximum space for

the stowage of ammunition. The nose of the lower hull originally consisted of three separate pieces bolted together, but late production versions had either a one-piece nose or a composite rolled/cast nose (Sherman I hybrid), with the cast section extending from the differential housing to the forward edge of the turret ring.

The power unit was the Wright or Continental R-975, a nine-cylinder air-cooled radial engine de-rated to produce 400bhp from 15,945cc (973in³); early tanks used the EC2 version of the power unit, constructed by Wright, but this was subsequently superseded by the Continental-built C1 version. Mounted at the rear, the engine was connected to a five-speed gearbox by means of a long propeller shaft running the length of the hull; the differential unit was bolted inside the nose casting, driving the front sprockets. The M4E1 was a development version for the M4A6, powered by a Caterpillar D-200 radial diesel engine. Most M4 variants were fitted with the vertical volute spring suspension system (VVSS). This was redesigned in mid-1942 with rear-mounted track-return rollers to reduce the incidence of spring failure, and the new suspension was fitted to tanks from January 1943. The heavier-duty horizontal volute spring suspension system (HVSS) was fitted to the final 841 examples of the 105mm gun-equipped variant.

The main gun was the 75mm M3, initially in the M34 mount but later in the modified M34A1 mount which had a wider mantlet. The M4 was also used as a mount for the 105mm howitzer (Sherman IB and IBY, the latter with HVSS suspension).

By the time production of the variant ended in January 1944, total production of the M4 amounted to 6,748 examples with the 75mm gun, of which somewhere around 1,600 were of the composite-hull type, and 1,641 fitted with the 105mm howitzer.

M4A1

Aside from the one-piece cast upper hull, combined with a riveted lower hull 'borrowed' from the M3, the M4A1 – described by the British as the Sherman II – differed little from the base model M4. It was actually the first variant into production, with the first examples

constructed for the British Army by Lima Locomotive. The first tank off the line, which was retained in the USA for testing, used the early T6 upper hull casting with the side access apertures welded up, but for all subsequent production the side doors were eliminated. Early examples were fitted with the short-barrelled 75mm M2 gun taken from the earlier M3 medium tank, with

ABOVE The chalked legend on the side of the hull says that this is an M4E5 – this was the prototype for the M4 equipped with the 105mm howitzer. *(Tank Museum)*

BELOW With its turtle-shaped cast hull there is no mistaking the M4A1, which like the M4 was powered by the Wright or Continental radial engine. This example with a 75mm gun is an outside exhibit at the Museum of the Battle of Normandy at Bayeux. Note the grousers designed to increase the width of the tracks. *(Ian Young)*

a counterweight clamped around the muzzle, and had two 0.30in Browning machine guns in the lower front area of the hull, one of which was eliminated in March 1942. The 75mm M2 was quickly superseded by the 75mm M3 gun, and then, from 1943, by the 76mm M1 in an improved turret with an integral counterweight (Sherman IIA).

The M4A1E8 variant (Sherman IIAY) was fitted with the horizontal volute spring suspension system (HVSS).

Production of the M4A1 started in February 1942 at Lima Locomotive; Pressed Steel started the following month, and Pacific Car & Foundry joined the fray in June 1942. By the time production ended in December 1943, a total of 9,707 examples had been built – 6,281 with the 75mm gun and 3,426 with the 76mm weapon.

M4A2

Like the base model M4, the M4A2 (Sherman III) was constructed with a welded hull, and was the first tank into production at the newly constructed Fisher Tank Grand Blanc plant. It was subsequently also produced by American Locomotive, Baldwin Locomotive, Federal Machine & Welder and Pullman-Standard, with a total of 10,968 built between April 1942 and June 1945: 8,053 of these were fitted with the 75mm gun, and 2,915 with the 76mm (Sherman IIIA). As with the M4A1 variant, later models (M4A2E8, or Sherman IIIAY) were fitted with the horizontal volute spring suspension system.

The major difference between the M4A2 and what had gone before lay in the choice of power plant, with the Wright radial engine of the M4 and M4A1 variants replaced by a GM Detroit Diesel 6046D twin diesel engine, producing 410bhp from a total of 13,962cc (852in^3). Most went to Britain and the Soviet Union under the Lend-Lease scheme.

Between October 1944 and April 1945 some 75 redundant M4A2s of the British Army had their turrets and armament removed and were converted to armoured personnel carriers (APC) to accommodate ten men, in which guise they were dubbed 'Kangaroos'.

M4A3

The welded-hull M4A3 (Sherman IV, though few were deployed outside the US Army) was constructed by the Ford Motor Company, Detroit Tank Arsenal and Fisher Tank Grand Blanc. The hull was similar to the M4A2 but was constructed from fewer components, which meant that less welding was required, and all M4A3s were fitted with a one-piece cast nose. The first example was completed by Ford in late May 1942 and shipped to the GM proving ground for trials.

Regardless of manufacturer, all M4A3s were powered by a Ford GAA V8 petrol engine producing 500bhp from a capacity of 18,026cc (1,100in^3). The GAA engine was the only Sherman power unit that had been specifically designed as a tank engine, and it proved itself to be trouble-free in operation. For this reason the M4A3 was the preferred variant of the US Army, and underwent the largest number of modifications and changes. The type remained in US Army service for a further ten years after the end of the war and no M4A3s were supplied under Lend-Lease until late 1944.

Early examples were fitted with the heavy-duty vertical volute spring suspension system (VVSS); the later M4A3E8 – called the 'Easy Eight' by GIs – and the M4A3E9 were both fitted with the horizontal volute spring suspension system. A 'W' suffix (eg M4A3W) indicated that there were wet ammunition stowage facilities.

Built in small numbers (254 units) by Fisher Tank Grand Blanc in the spring of 1944, the M4A3E2 assault tank – sometimes unofficially called 'Jumbo' or 'Cobra King' by the GIs – was intended for infantry support during the invasion of Europe when the US Army believed that

BELOW Posing outside the Ford tank plant at Highland Park, this is a factory-fresh M4A3 with the one-piece cast differential housing, possibly the first such tank to be assembled. The M4A3 was powered by the mighty Ford GAA V8 petrol engine, the only Sherman power plant to have been designed specifically for use in tanks. *(Ford Motor Company)*

RIGHT Rear view of the Ford GAA-engined M4A3 with the turret hatches open; early examples were fitted with the heavy-duty vertical volute spring suspension system (VVSS), but this was subsequently superseded by the improved HVSS system. The M4A3 was the variant most favoured by the US Army. *(Tank Museum)*

BELOW Late production Ford-engined M4A3 fitted with the 105mm howitzer; note the wide tracks and horizontal volute spring suspension. *(Tank Museum)*

they would come up against large numbers of German heavy tanks. The hull was up-armoured on all surfaces, and the tank was equipped with a new heavy turret mounting the 75mm M3 gun; some units replaced this in the field with the 76mm gun. The considerable increase in weight reduced the top speed to 22mph (36kmh).

Production of the M4A3 ended in March 1945, by which time a total of 12,342 had been

RIGHT M4A3E8 was the prototype for the M4A3 HVSS, fitted with the 76mm M1 gun. The type was built by Detroit Tank Arsenal between August 1944 and May 1945. *(Tank Museum)*

for the M3A4 medium tank. Producing around 425bhp from a combined capacity of 20,533cc (1,253in^3), the A-57 engine consisted of five six-cylinder banks assembled around a common crankcase, with ring gears on each of the crankshafts to feed the power of each set of cylinders into a single central shaft. The complexity of the engine was such that troops apparently dubbed it the 'egg beater' or the 'Dionne Quints', the latter nickname chosen for the 1934-born quintuplets who were the first known to have survived infancy. The size of the engine necessitated lengthening the engine compartment, with the tracks similarly extended and the centre and rear bogies relocated. Although the M4A4 was not accepted by the US Army for service overseas, the engine eventually proved itself to be reliable, and those M4A4s that were not supplied to the British Army under the Lend-Lease arrangements were retained for training in the USA.

Production of the M4A4 started in July 1942, with the last of 7,499 tanks coming off the production line in September 1943. The M4A4 was the first Sherman variant to be discontinued, and although it was subsequently used as the basis of the British Firefly, using the 17-pounder (76.2mm) gun, it was never fitted with the American 76mm M1 gun.

constructed. Of these, 4,761 were fitted with the 75mm gun, 4,542 with the 76mm (M4A3E4 or Sherman IVA), and a further 3,039 with the 105mm howitzer (Sherman IVB).

M4A4

The M4A4 (Sherman V) was constructed around a welded hull consisting of just five separate components, and was powered by Chrysler's A-57 30-cylinder engine, a unique multi-bank petrol engine that had originally been developed

RIGHT **An M4A4 that has been fitted with deep-water wading ducts and appears to have been given an overall coating of concrete or plaster, perhaps to discourage the attachment of magnetic mines. The Germans coated their tanks with a paste called *Zimmerit* for this purpose, and it is known that after the war the British carried out trials of a similar material, so this may well be a photograph of such a trial.**
(Tank Museum)

M4A5

Originally to be described as the 'Buffalo', the designation M4A5 was assigned to the Canadian-built Grizzly tank, which was based on the cast-hull Sherman M4A1 powered by the Wright or Continental R-975 radial engine, and armed with the American 75mm gun. The name Buffalo was dropped in deference to the British 79th Armoured Division, which used a buffalo as its divisional sign.

The Grizzly differed from the standard M4A1 Sherman by having a thicker hull (75mm rather than 51mm) and in having 17 teeth on the drive sprocket rather than 13, in order to match the shorter-pitch Canadian dry-pin track (CDP). The stowage arrangements followed British rather than American practice, and there was a British Number 19 radio set in a turret bustle. It had originally been planned that 1,200 Grizzlys would be built at the Montreal Locomotive Works, replacing the Ram II on the production line, and some 80% of the parts required had been ordered by the middle of January 1943. However, in the event just 188 were produced between August and December 1943, with the first batch of 23 delivered during the third week of October.

Following the cessation of Grizzly production the line was switched to building the Sexton self-propelled gun Mk II, which used a similar chassis. The Grizzly hull was also used as the basis for the Skink 20mm quad anti-aircraft tank, just three examples of which were constructed.

M4A6

The M4A6 started life with the designation M4E1 and was effectively an M4A4 hull into which had been fitted a diesel multi-fuel version of the Wright G-200 radial engine, the conversion work on the engine having been carried out by the Caterpillar Tractor Company. Designated D-200, and later known as the RD-1820, the engine had a maximum power output of 450bhp and was equally capable of running on diesel or petrol fuels ... or, for that matter, almost anything that would burn!

Caterpillar installed 20 of these engines into standard M4A4 hulls during late 1942 and, following a period of trials, the tank went into production as the M4A6 at the Detroit Tank Arsenal in late 1943. The production vehicles used the late version of the M4A4 hull with a one-piece cast front, with *appliqué* armour on the hull sides. Production ceased in February 1944 after just 75 examples had been constructed.

LEFT The Canadian-built M4A5 used a similar cast hull to the M4A1, albeit of greater thickness, and was similarly powered by the Wright or Continental radial engine. Just 188 were built, all of them during 1943. *(Phil Royal)*

ABOVE Detail of the armoured rear bustle of the Sherman Firefly designed to allow installation of the radio in a position that would be safe from the recoil of the much more powerful 17-pounder (76.2mm) gun. *(Tank Museum)*

ABOVE The British Sherman Firefly was armed with a 17-pounder (76.2mm) gun, laying on its side in a new mount. The turret was modified by the addition of a new loader's hatch and by cutting a hole in the rear wall and welding an armoured box on the back to provide space for the radio set. The most common basis for the conversion was the M4A4 (Sherman V). *(Tank Museum)*

British Army variants

Despite the differences in nomenclature (already noted), Sherman tanks in British service differed little from their US Army counterparts, any modifications being confined mostly to stowage provision and the use of the British Number 19 radio set and antennae in place of radio sets from the US Signals Corps SCR series. Most British Shermans were also fitted with either a smoke launcher on the turret roof, or a pair of smoke generators on the turret sides.

The Sherman Firefly was an exclusively British variant, with the turret modified to mount the 17-pounder (76.2mm) Ordnance quick-firing (OQF) gun in an attempt to provide sufficient firepower to take on the better-armed and better-armoured late model German tanks. Against considerable initial opposition, the modification was initiated by Sir Claude Gibb, a civilian working for the Ministry of Supply as the Director General of Weapon and Instrument Production; he was supported by Major George Brighty and Lieutenant-Colonel Witheridge. Early experiments had mounted the 17-pounder on the Cromwell chassis, in the form of the Challenger, but by June 1943 it was obvious that considerable further development work would be required, and it was proposed that the already-proven Sherman might form a better mount for the weapon.

The early conversion work was carried out by Vickers-Armstrong using an M4 (Sherman

I). Production started in early 1944, with the Royal Ordnance Factories converting somewhere between 2,100 and 2,350 vehicles. There is some dispute as to exactly which Sherman variants were converted, but it is possible that Fireflys – or Mayflys, as some older sources suggest – were constructed using Sherman I, II, IV and V hulls, with the Sherman V being the most common. A small number of Canadian-built Grizzlys were also converted for training purposes. The Firefly conversion was identified by adding a 'C' suffix to the British designation (*eg* Sherman VC).

Israeli 'Super Shermans'

During the 25 years or so following the end of World War Two the Israeli Defence Force (IDF) acquired Shermans from various sources, eventually operating a fleet of more than 700, some of which had been captured from neighbouring Arab states. As these ageing warriors began to look obsolete, the IDF initiated a programme of upgrading, fitting the tanks with new guns and engines.

The chosen gun was the CN-75-50, a French high-velocity 75mm weapon based on the German *KwK.42* L/70 that had been used in the Panther tank in World War Two. The conversion work was carried out in IDF workshops and started in 1953/54, initially using M4A4 hulls that had already had their Chrysler engines replaced by the more conventional Wright or Continental R-975 radial engine. The converted turrets and the guns were supplied direct from France. After some 50 or so vehicles had been converted a switch was made to later M4A3 hulls fitted with HVSS suspension, and at the same time the old radial engines were ousted in favour of a 460bhp Cummins VT-8-460Bi V8 turbocharged diesel. The result was designated the Sherman M50, although it is often described as the 'Super Sherman'.

During the 1960s a further 180 IDF M4A1 HVSS Shermans were up-gunned with a shortened version of the French CN-105F1 gun, which was built under licence in Israel, as well as being fitted with the Cummins diesel engine. These tanks, which can be recognised by the huge turret bustle required to counterbalance the gun, were designated Sherman M51 and sometimes described as the 'Isherman'. The first example was shown in public in May 1965 and a number remained in service into the 1980s.

Specialised tanks

The sheer numbers of Shermans available made the tank a prime candidate for conversion to various specialised roles, including armoured recovery vehicle, flame-thrower, rocket-launcher, 'dozer tank and mine-clearance vehicle. In the lead-up to the D-Day landings the British Army, particularly, favoured the Sherman as the basis for a range of so-called 'funnies', each tasked with overcoming a particular problem. These vehicles made an enormous contribution to the success of the landings.

Whilst most of the conversions were 'official', others – including the mounting of a double-track assault bridge on the Sherman's nose – were field modifications made in response to the situation on the ground. See Table 4 on page 45 for a full list of Sherman adaptations, both experimental and production.

Armoured recovery vehicles

The US Army's M32 tank recovery vehicle was standardised in September 1943 and was constructed around the hull of the standard M4, with the pilot vehicle built by Lima Locomotive. The turret and gun were removed and replaced by a fixed superstructure, together with an

ABOVE Israeli M50 'Super Sherman', equipped with the French CN-75-50 high-velocity 75mm gun. Conversion work started in 1953/54, initially using M4A4 hulls that had been fitted with Wright or Continental R-975 radial engines. Later examples used M4A3 HVSS hulls and were fitted with a Cummins VT-8-460Bi V8 turbocharged diesel engine. *(Roland Groom, Tank Museum)*

81mm mortar intended to lay smoke. A 60,000lb (27,275kg) winch was installed in the fighting compartment, and a pivoting A-frame jib was mounted on the hull in such a way that it could be used in conjunction with the winch.

BELOW Based on the M4A4, the British Sherman-based recovery vehicle, designated the ARV Mk II, mounted a fixed turret in which was installed a dummy gun, with a Croft 60-ton winch installed in the fighting compartment. There was a detachable 3.5-ton winch at the front, a fixed 9.5-ton winch at the rear, and a substantial earth anchor. *(Warehouse Collection)*

Table 1: Major Sherman gun tank variants

Designation US Army	Designation British Army	Date	Engine	Suspension	Hull construction and max thickness of armour	Main gun	Battle weight
M4 variants							
M4	Sherman I	1942	Wright or Continental R-975 radial; 400bhp	VVSS**	welded; hull, 51mm; turret, 76mm	75mm M3	n/a
M4 (composite)	Sherman I hybrid	1942	Wright or Continental R-975 radial; 400bhp	VVSS	rolled/cast; hull, 51mm; turret, 89mm	75mm M3	66,900lb (30,409kg)
M4 (105mm)	Sherman IB	1943	Wright or Continental R-975 radial; 400bhp	VVSS	welded; hull, 64mm; turret, 91mm	105mm M4	69,400lb (31,545kg)
M4 (105mm)	Sherman IBY	1944	Wright or Continental R-975 radial; 400bhp	HVSS***	welded; hull, 51mm; turret, 76mm	105mm M4	69,400lb (31,545kg)
M4E1(ii)	–	1942	Caterpillar D-200 (RD-1820) radial diesel; 450bhp	VVSS	welded; hull, 51mm; turret, 76mm	75mm M3	n/a
M4A1 variants							
M4A1	Sherman II	1942	Wright or Continental R-975 radial; 400bhp	VVSS	cast; hull, 51mm; turret, 76mm	75mm M2; 75mm M3	66,800lb (30,364kg)
M4A1E4 (76mm)	Sherman IIA	1944	Wright or Continental R-975 radial; 400bhp	VVSS	cast; hull, 108mm; turret, 91mm	76mm M1	70,600lb (32,091kg)
M4A1E8 (76mm)	Sherman IIAY	1944	Wright or Continental R-975 radial; 400bhp	HVSS	cast; hull, 108mm; turret, 91mm	76mm M1	70,600lb (32,091kg)
M4A2 variants							
M4A2	Sherman III	1942	GM 6-71 6046D diesel; 410bhp (2x 205bhp)	VVSS	welded; hull, 108mm; turret, 89mm	75mm M3	69,000lb (31,364kg)
M4A2 (76mm)	Sherman IIIA	1944	GM 6-71 6046D diesel; 410bhp (2x 205bhp)	VVSS	welded; hull, 108mm; turret, 89mm	76mm M1	73,400lb (33,364kg)
M4A2E8 (76mm)	Sherman IIIAY	1944	GM 6-71 6046D diesel; 410bhp (2x 205bhp)	HVSS	welded; hull, 108mm; turret, 89mm	76mm M1	73,400lb (33,364kg)
M4A3 variants							
M4A3	Sherman IV	1942	Ford GAA V8 petrol; 450bhp	VVSS	welded; hull, 51mm; turret, 89mm	75mm M3	66,700lb (30,318kg)
M4A3 (105mm)	Sherman IVB	1942	Ford GAA V8 petrol; 450bhp	VVSS	welded; hull, 108mm; turret, 91mm	105mm M4	72,900lb (33,136kg)
M4A3E2 'Jumbo'	–	1944	Ford GAA V8 petrol; 450bhp	VVSS	welded; hull, 140mm; turret, 178mm	75mm M3; 76mm M1*	84,000lb (38,182kg)
M4A3E4 (76mm)	Sherman IVAY	1944	Ford GAA V8 petrol; 450bhp	VVSS	welded; hull, 108mm; turret, 89mm	76mm M1	69,600lb (31,636kg)
M4A3E8 (76mm)	Sherman IVAY	1944	Ford GAA V8 petrol; 450bhp	HVSS	welded; hull, 108mm; turret, 89mm	76mm M1	74,200lb (33,727kg)
M4A3E9 (105mm)	Sherman IVBY	1942	Ford GAA V8 petrol; 450bhp	HVSS	welded; hull, 108mm; turret, 91mm	105mm M4	72,900lb (33,136kg)
M4A4 variants							
M4A4	Sherman V	1942	Chrysler A-57 multi-bank; 425bhp	VVSS	welded; hull, 51mm; turret, 76mm	75mm M3	69,700lb (31,682kg)
M4A5 variants							
M4A5 Grizzly	–	1943	Wright or Continental R-975 radial; 400bhp	VVSS	cast; hull, 75mm; turret, 76mm	75mm M3	66,500lb (30,227kg)
M4A6 variants							
M4A6	Sherman VII	1943	Caterpillar D-200 (RD-1820) radial diesel; 450bhp	VVSS	welded; hull, 108mm; turret, 89mm	75mm M3	70,000lb (31,818kg)

* 76mm gun sometimes fitted as field modification.
** Vertical volute spring suspension system.
*** Horizontal volute spring suspension system.

LEFT **Formed in 1956, the post-war German *Bundeswehr* often used US Army equipment. The photograph shows an M74 tank recovery vehicle (*Berge Pz* M74), which was based on the M4A3 HVSS chassis, lifting the Rolls-Royce engine from a British Army Saracen armoured personnel carrier.** *(Tank Museum)*

BELOW The beach armoured recovery vehicle (BARV) had raised sides to enable it to operate in up to eight feet (2.4m) of water. Lacking a gun, but well protected against gunfire, the BARV was designed to rescue vehicles that had become bogged down on a landing beach. *(Warehouse Collection)*

Additional tow points and equipment stowage facilities were also provided.

Other variants included the M32B1, which was based on the hull of the M4A1; the M32B2, which used the M4A2 hull; the M32B3, based on the hull of the M4A3, including some examples with HVSS suspension; and finally the M32B4, which used the M4A4 hull. The M32B1 was also converted into a prime mover by the removal of the A-frame in order to provide an artillery towing vehicle; in this form it was designated M34. The M32 was replaced by the M74 tank recovery vehicle from 1954, with some 1,000 examples produced over a two-year period by Bowen-McLaughlin-York, including some that were converted from redundant M32s.

Although the British Army also used the M32 recovery vehicle – describing it as the armoured recovery vehicle (ARV) Mk III – the workshops of the Royal Electrical and Mechanical Engineers (REME) also constructed a 'British' Sherman-based recovery vehicle. Known as the ARV Mk II, it mounted a fixed turret in which was installed a dummy gun, with a Croft 60-ton winch installed in the fighting compartment. There was a detachable 3.5-ton winch at the front, and a fixed 9.5-ton winch at the rear, as well as a substantial earth anchor.

Beach armoured recovery vehicle

Developed by the REME specifically for recovering drowned or disabled tanks from the D-Day beaches, the Sherman-based beach armoured recovery vehicle (BARV) had the turret and gun removed and the hull sides raised to allow the vehicle to wade in up to eight feet (2.4m) of water.

RIGHT Dating from 1945, the T31 demolition tank was an experimental vehicle mounting a 105mm howitzer and a pair of 7.2in (183mm) rocket launchers on a large fabricated turret. The vehicle did not enter production. *(Tank Museum)*

Demolition tank

The prototype T31 demolition tank was constructed in 1945 on the chassis of an M4A3 with HVSS suspension. A 105mm howitzer was mounted in a large fabricated turret, with a 7.2in (183mm) rocket-launcher to either side. There was no series production and the project was abandoned.

Duplex-drive amphibious tanks

The British Army had started to test amphibious tanks during World War One, but none had worked well enough for use in combat. Development continued during the interwar years, but it wasn't until June 1941 that Hungarian inventor Nicholas Straussler finally solved the problem of making tanks float. By fitting a folding canvas screen to a frame welded around the top of the hull, the displacement of the hull was increased, which allowed the tank to float hull-down in the

BELOW Duplex-drive (DD) Sherman with the wading screen collapsed and the propellers disengaged; some of the supporting struts that will hold the wading screen in the erect position can be seen behind the turret. The conversion was carried out using both M4A2 and M4A4 Sherman variants. *(Tank Museum)*

water. The screen was raised by compressed air and was secured by stays. A second drive system, which diverted power from the tracks to rear-mounted propellers, allowed the tanks to swim from landing craft to beach. In the water, steering was achieved by means of a rudder and by swivelling the propellers on a horizontal axis. It was this secondary drive system that gave the tanks their name of 'duplex drive', or DD.

Major General Percy Hobart of the British 79th Armoured Division was impressed by the principle of Straussler's folding screen and carried out trials in Portsmouth Harbour. The success of these trials led to the selection of the British Valentine for the development of the duplex-drive tank, and plans were also put in hand to convert Shermans for the same role.

The majority of the American, British and Canadian DD tank crews did their preliminary training using Valentines, but it soon became clear that the Sherman was more suitable for amphibious use, and the conversion was carried out using M4A2 (Sherman III) and M4A4 (Sherman V) variants. The increased weight of the Sherman, when compared to the Valentine, dictated an increase in the height of the canvas screen, and the drive to the propellers was taken from the rear sprockets using bevel gears, with the advantage that the tracks were running as soon as the tank touched the beach. The propellers were designed to hinge upwards when not in use.

DD Shermans were used very effectively on D-Day, although rough seas could, and did, drive them off course, particularly on the approach to Utah beach. DD Shermans were also used during the Rhine crossing in 1945.

Flame-thrower tanks

The British car manufacturer Lagonda Motors had constructed and demonstrated a portable flame-thrower device back in 1940. Although the first version had a range of little more than 100ft (30m), the company eventually managed to produce a unit that could pump burning petroleum fuel 350ft (107m). The initial application for what was indisputably a fearsome weapon was in the protection of shipping and airfields against low-level attack by aircraft, and experiments followed which were directed towards mounting the flame-thrower on either a truck chassis or a tracked vehicle. It was the latter work, at the end of July 1942, which saw the weapon adapted to allow it to be fitted to tanks, where it proved enormously effective against pillboxes and strongpoints.

Early development work was carried out on a pair of British Valentines, and then on a Churchill, in the latter case with the fuel carried in a trailer and the flame projector mounted on the hull front. It was this version which was selected for production, but the British and Canadian Armies also produced experimental flame-thrower Shermans under the names Ronson, Salamander and Adder.

The US Army too produced a number of flame-thrower devices designed to be mounted on the Sherman. In some cases the flame projector was used to replace the co-driver's periscope aperture or the hull machine gun, in other cases it replaced the main gun. In

late 1944 the US 2nd Armored Division also adapted four Shermans to mount the Churchill Crocodile flame-thrower.

Mine-clearing tanks

During World War Two huge numbers of anti-tank mines and even greater numbers of anti-personnel or land mines were laid by both sides, presenting considerable danger to advancing armies. All kinds of solutions to dealing with these mines were proposed, including explosive devices, flails, rollers and ploughs, all of them attached to modified tank hulls. Many were immediately dismissed as being impractical, never progressing beyond the experimental stage, but others were developed to the point where they were quite successful.

Of all of the mine-clearance devices developed during World War Two, the flail proved to be the most effective. Work on such a device had started back in 1939, when it

ABOVE Duplex-drive (DD) Sherman with the wading screen fully erected; note that in this view, the twin propeller screws are in the operating position. The DD Mk II differed only in detail from the original. *(Tank Museum)*

LEFT US Army M4A3 Sherman fitted with a flame-thrower firing through the main gun tube. The Allied flame-throwers were much feared by German soldiers, and with good reason! *(Warehouse Collection)*

Table 2:
Development vehicles and major production changes

Designation	Date	Description
M4 variants		
M4E1(i)	1942	M4A1 with 76mm T1 gun; modified turret with rear bustle to accommodate recoil.
M4E1(ii)	1943	M4A4 with Caterpillar D-200 (RD1820) diesel engine as development vehicle for M4A6.
M4E2	1943	M4A4 with 24in (610mm) wide T80 tracks and HVSS suspension.
M4E3	1943	M4A4 with Chrysler V12 engine.
M4E4	1943	M4 with 24in (610mm) wide tracks and experimental torsion-bar suspension.
M4E5	1943	Prototype for M4 (105mm).
M4E6	1943	Experimental vehicle mounting T23 cast turret and 76mm M1A1 gun, and with wet ammunition stowage.
M4E7	1943	M4A1 with Ford GAA engine in place of Wright or Continental R-975 radial engine.
M4E8	1943	M4A3 with HVSS suspension and 76mm M1 gun.
M4E9	1943	M4 with spaced VVSS suspension and track grousers.
M4A1 variants		
M4A1E1	–	M4A1 with insulated crew compartment and air-conditioning equipment for desert warfare.
M4A1E2	–	M4A1 with recording odograph and infrared lights for night fighting.
M4A1E3	–	M4A1 with Spicer Model 95 torque converter.
M4A1E5	–	M4A1 with upgraded Wright or Continental R-975 radial engine, and with increased fuel capacity; adopted for late production.
M4A1E8	1944	Prototype for MAA1 with HVSS suspension, 76mm M1 gun, and wet ammunition stowage; subsequently adopted for late production.
M4A1E9	1943	M4A1 with spaced VVSS suspension and track grousers.
M4A2 variants		
M4A2E1	1943	Experimental vehicle with single GM V8 diesel engine in place of twin GM 6046D diesels.
M4A2E4		M4A2 with 24in (610mm) wide tracks and experimental torsion-bar suspension.
M4A2E9	1943	M4A2 with spaced VVSS suspension and track grousers.
M4A3 variants		
M4A3E1	1944	M4A3 with Spicer Model 95 torque converter.
M4A3E2	1944	Prototype for heavy assault tank; known as 'Jumbo' or 'Cobra King'.
M4A3E3	1944	Prototype with 47° frontal armour.
M4A3E4	1944	Prototype for M4A3 with 76mm M1 gun.
M4A3E8	1944	Prototype for M4A3 (76mm) with HVSS suspension and wet ammunition stowage.
M4A3E9	1944	M4A2 with spaced VVSS suspension and track grousers.
M4A4 variants		
M4A4E1	1942	Prototype for M4A4 (105mm).

was proposed by the British Mechanization Board that anti-tank mines could be exploded by weights attached to the ends of spring-steel strips on a revolving drum carried ahead of a tank. The development work was carried out by AEC Limited, and it was soon found that the device would be more effective if the spring-steel strips and weights were replaced by revolving chains. Initial trials of a device described as Baron Mk I were carried out using a Matilda II tank, still with its turret and gun. This was followed by Baron Mk II, which used a hydraulic raising and lowering system for the rotor. Meanwhile, a simpler flail device had been developed in the Middle East during 1942, dubbed Scorpion, and by the end of July 1943 it was issued for user trials. Although the original Scorpion was eventually abandoned, by the middle of June 1943 there had been considerable progress with mounting a modified version on a Sherman tank and, known as Crab, this became the most successful of the flails. The first prototype was ready for trials in September 1943 when the design was 'frozen', with work starting on the first production vehicle. User trials started at the end of October 1943 and the system proved effective at destroying mines and cutting barbed wire.

Other approaches included explosive devices, ploughs and rollers. The Sherman Snake and Conger consisted of a long hosepipe or cylinder of explosive intended to be pushed across a minefield and detonated remotely, thus exploding the mines ahead of an advancing tank. The Snake could clear a path about 30in (762mm) wide, certainly sufficient to allow infantry to pass through safely. A similar device, dubbed Tapeworm and consisting of a flexible hosepipe that could be filled with liquid explosive once in position, before being detonated, was designed to be towed across the minefield by a flail tank.

Tank-mounted ploughs for anti-tank mines had been first developed before World War Two by John Fowler & Company, but the device never lived up to its original promise. The most successful type of plough, which was developed and tested by the 79th Armoured Division in conjunction with a Sherman, was the Bullshorn, but it was eventually abandoned in favour of the flail.

ABOVE The Lobster was a one-off device using the same type of flails and rotor as the earlier Baron flail devised by South African officer Major Abraham Du Toit, and was the forerunner of the successful Crab. *(Tank Museum)*

ABOVE Dating from 1943, the so-called Pram Scorpion was a flail device constructed by Samuel Butler Limited of Leeds. The flails were driven via chains on the front sprockets of the tank rather than by an auxiliary engine. Never entirely successful, it was replaced by the Sherman Crab. *(Tank Museum)*

BELOW Based on the M4A4, complete with its turret and main gun, the Sherman Crab was derived from the Pram Scorpion and was the most successful of the mine flails. The flail rotor was driven by a chain, and thence by shafts, and the supporting arms could be raised and lowered hydraulically. *(Warehouse Collection)*

Anti-mine rollers had already been developed in the years immediately following World War One, and by 1937 John Fowler & Company had successfully trialled an anti-mine roller attachment (AMRA) which consisted of a girder frame projecting ahead of the tank carrying four heavy rollers. This idea was also adapted for the Sherman-mounted anti-mine reconnaissance castor roller (AMRCR), which proved useful against anti-personnel mines. Rollers with projecting spikes were tested experimentally in the Middle East, and one such device, dubbed

RIGHT Improvised flail developed by the US Marines in the Pacific theatre using parts of the M1 'dozer kit. *(Warehouse Collection)*

RIGHT The Canadian indestructible roller device (CIRD) consisted of two rollers of solid forged armour-quality steel, 16in (400mm) wide and 26in (660mm) diameter, each weighing one ton and carried on long arms, arranged to pivot about eight feet (2,440mm) ahead of the tank in front of each track. Exploding mines caused the arms to lift, rotating the bracket that held the roller; the forward movement of the tank would return the roller to the operating position. *(Tank Museum)*

RIGHT The T10 mine exploder consisted of three huge roller units mounted on articulating arms and driven by the hull of an M4A3 tank from which the standard tracks and suspension had been removed. The device proved unwieldy in use and development was abandoned in late 1944. *(Tank Museum)*

RIGHT Period colour photograph of Aunt Jemima, the most widely used mine exploder of the US Army during World War Two. It consisted of two huge rollers, each consisting of five 10ft (3,050mm) steel discs chain-driven from the front sprockets of the tank. A total of 75 examples were constructed. *(Tank Museum)*

Porcupine, was tested in Britain in conjunction with a Sherman.

The most successful of the rollers was the Canadian indestructible roller device (CIRD), which had been constructed at the Canadian Army Workshops at Borden, Hampshire, during 1943. The CIRD consisted of two huge rollers of solid forged armour-quality steel, 16in (400mm) wide and 26in (660mm) in diameter, each weighing one ton. The rollers were carried on long arms, arranged to pivot about 8ft (2.4m) ahead of the tank in front of each track, and were suspended on a substantial cross-shaft, with helical springs provided to position the trailing arms. Following a series of trials, the CIRD was deemed to be sufficiently promising to warrant further investigation and possible production, and in December arrangements were made to fit the device to a Sherman, with designs for both Churchill and Sherman tanks standardised in May 1945.

Although roller devices were subsequently superseded by the more successful flails, some development continued, with devices such as Rodent, Lulu, Aunt Jemima, Earthworm and Centipede achieving varying degrees of success. The Lulu system was particularly interesting since the device attempted to adapt the successful Polish electro-magnetic mine-detection system for use with a tank, whilst the remote mine roller T10 actually replaced the track system of the tank with three huge rollers mounted tricycle-fashion on swing arms.

Rocket-launcher tanks

Various rocket-launcher mounts were developed by the US Army for use with the M4 series of vehicles, but just two of these, the T34 Calliope and T40 Whizbang, saw any real combat use. Developed in 1943 and first used by the US 2nd Armored Division in France in 1944, Calliope consisted of 60 4.6in (117mm) rocket tubes mounted in a frame above the turret; the mount was designed to rotate with the turret

and the tubes were elevated by a mechanical link to the gun barrel. Whizbang was used in combat in 1944/45 and consisted of 20 7.2in (183mm) rockets in an hydraulically elevated box mount.

Other applications for the M4 chassis

The M4 hull, chassis and running gear were also used as the basis for a range of self-propelled guns, including the M7B1 105mm gun motor carriage, the M40 155mm gun motor carriage, the M36 90mm gun motor carriage, the M43 8in howitzer motor carriage, the T51 25-pounder gun motor carriage, and the T94 10in howitzer motor carriage. It was also

ABOVE Lulu was a British adaptation of the Polish electro-magnetic mine-detection system for use with a tank. Three wooden rollers were carried on booms ahead of and behind the tank; mine detector coils in the drums signalled to the operator whenever the tank drove over a mine. The device was never used in anger.
(Tank Museum)

RIGHT T34 Calliope multiple rocket launcher of the US Army 80th Division, photographed in March 1945. The Calliope carried 60 launchers for 4.6in rockets in a frame mounted above the turret. *(Tank Museum)*

adapted for the M10 tank destroyer, the M10A1 prime mover and the T30 cargo carrier, and there were other experimental vehicles which never entered production.

M7B1 105mm howitzer motor carriage

Work on the M7 105mm howitzer gun motor carriage started in June 1941 and the original plan was to employ the lower hull and running gear of the M3 medium tank. Two prototypes were constructed in this form, mounting the M1A2 105mm howitzer. Production started in 1942 at Lima Locomotive, but in September 1943, when the M3 was superseded by the M4, production was switched to the hull of the M4A3, and the designation was amended to M7B1 – the British dubbed this vehicle the Priest. During 'Operation Totalise', which was intended to help in the capture of the French

city of Caen during August 1944, the Canadian Army used a number of Priests which had been stripped of their guns – or 'defrocked', as some would have it – and converted into Kangaroo armoured personnel carriers.

A total of 826 examples were built by Pressed Steel between March 1944 and February 1945, and a further 127 (including some M7 variants) by Federal Machine & Welder.

M10 tank destroyer

Development of the M10 tank destroyer started in April 1942 as the T35. Following the rejection of the first prototype, which was based on an M4A2 hull with an open-topped turret, a second vehicle was constructed (T35E1) using the lower part of the M4A2 hull, on which was mounted a new, relatively lightweight angled superstructure together with a five-sided open-topped turret with a huge counterweight at

Table 3:
Major gun tank modifications

Designation	Original basis	Date	Engine	Suspension	Main gun
British Army modifications					
Sherman IC Firefly	M4 (composite)	1944	Wright or Continental R-975 radial; 400bhp	VVSS	17-pounder Mk IV, VII
Sherman IIC Firefly	M4A1	1944	Wright or Continental R-975 radial; 400bhp	VVSS	17-pounder Mk IV, VII
Sherman IVC Firefly	M4A3	1944	Ford GAA V8 petrol; 450bhp	VVSS, HVSS	17-pounder Mk IV, VII
Sherman VC Firefly	M4A4	1944	Chrysler A-57 multi-bank; 370bhp	VVSS	17-pounder Mk IV, VII
Grizzly Firefly	M4A5	1944	Wright or Continental R-975 radial; 400bhp	VVSS	17-pounder Mk IV, VII
Israeli Defence Force modifications					
M50 (prototype)	M4A2	1955	GM 6046D diesel; 410bhp (2x 205bhp)	VVSS	75mm CN75-50
M50 Mk 1	M4A4	1956	Wright or Continental R-975 radial; 400bhp	VVSS	75mm M3
M50 Mk 2	M4A3	1960	Cummins VT-8-460Bi V8 diesel; 460bhp	VVSS, HVSS	75mm CN75-50
M51	M4A1	1963	Cummins VT-8-460Bi V8 diesel; 460bhp	HVSS	105mm CN-105F1 (in improved T23 turret)

the rear. The main armament was the 3in M7 anti-tank gun, a highly accurate weapon with a very flat trajectory. The design was standardised in June 1942 and production started in September of that year. Both M4A2 and M4A3 chassis were used during the production run, the latter designated M10A1, and a total of 6,706 examples had been constructed by the time the line was closed down in November 1943. Fisher Tank Grand Blanc built 5,668 examples of both the M10 and M10A1, whilst the Ford Motor Company built 738 M10A1s.

The turret of the M10 was always unbalanced, and the T72 was an attempt to overcome this shortcoming. The turret was based on that of the T23 medium tank, whilst the 76mm gun was replaced by a 3in weapon. The project was eventually abandoned in favour of the M18 Hellcat.

Examples of both the M10 and the M10A1 were supplied to the British Army, where they were dubbed the Wolverine. From late 1944 most of those remaining in service were modified by having the 3in M7 gun replaced by the more powerful British OQF 17-pounder (76.2mm). In this form the vehicle was described as the Achilles, and many remained in service well into the post-war period. Others had the gun and turret removed and were converted to artillery tractors.

M36 90mm gun motor carriage
Development of the M36 76mm gun motor carriage started in late 1942, with the first

prototype completed in early 1943. It consisted essentially of the hull of the M10A1 tank destroyer mounting a 90mm M3 high-velocity anti-tank gun. However, the turret proved to be unsuitable for the size of the gun and it was necessary to design a new, larger turret before the vehicle was standardised in June 1944. A total of 1,218 examples were constructed by Fisher Tank Grand Blanc, American Locomotive Company, Massey-Harris, and Montreal Locomotive Works, with production ending in June 1945; most were converted from existing M10s.

The M36B1 also mounted the 90mm gun, but utilised the hull of the M4A3; 187 examples were constructed by Fisher Tank Grand Blanc in late 1944. The M36B2 utilised the hull of

BELOW The M10 tank destroyer used the lower part of the M4A2 or M4A3 hull, on which was mounted a new lightweight angled superstructure carrying a five-sided open-topped turret for the 3in M7 anti-tank gun. *(Warehouse Collection)*

RIGHT The M36 gun motor carriage, or tank destroyer, consisted essentially of the hull of the M10A1 tank destroyer, which itself was based on the M4A2, mounting the 90mm M3 high-velocity anti-tank gun in a completely new turret. *(Simon Thomson)*

ABOVE Mounting the British 25-pounder, the Sexton was based on the lower hull and running gear of the Canadian M4A5 Grizzly. The turret and main gun were removed and replaced by a new superstructure that allowed full elevation for the 25-pounder. *(Simon Thomson)*

the M10, with 237 examples constructed by American Locomotive.

M40 155mm gun motor carriage

Mounting a huge 155mm gun, the M40 gun motor carriage was based on a widened M4A3 chassis with HVSS suspension. A pilot model, designated T83, was produced in March 1944,

RIGHT The T52 gun motor carriage was designed for the anti-aircraft role, and the standard turret was replaced by a large ball-mount carrying either two 40mm anti-aircraft guns or a single 40mm cannon flanked by a pair of 0.50in machine guns. *(Tank Museum)*

with production of the first 300 vehicles by Pressed Steel starting in January 1945. The design was standardised in March 1945 and the order was subsequently increased to 600, but only 311 were completed before the end of the war saw the contract cancelled.

M43 8in howitzer motor carriage

Initially identified as the T89 gun motor carriage, the pilot model for the M43 was completed in March 1945 by converting an M40 to carry the 9in howitzer. Although the design was standardised in August 1945, just 48 examples were constructed.

Sexton self-propelled gun

The British Sexton self-propelled gun used the Canadian Grizzly hull with the turret and main gun removed to provide a mount for the British 25-pounder. There were two 'marks', with detail variations, and a total of 2,150 were constructed by Montreal Locomotive Works, many remaining in service with the Portuguese and South African Armies into the 1980s.

T30 cargo carrier

Although it never progressed beyond the prototype stage, the T30 armoured cargo carrier was designed as a limber for the M40 155mm gun motor carriage. Five examples were constructed by Pressed Steel using the welded hull of the late model M4, with HVSS suspension.

T51 25-pounder gun motor carriage

Dating from 1943, the T51 25-pounder gun motor carriage was an American attempt at fitting the British 25-pounder gun into the M4 Sherman chassis, in much the same way as the US 155mm gun had been used to produce the M7 Priest. The development programme was set back by the destruction of the gun mount on the prototype during the first live-firing exercise.

T52 multiple gun motor carriage

Based on the M4 chassis, and dating from July 1942, the T52 multiple gun motor carriage was designed for an anti-aircraft role. The standard turret was removed and replaced by a large ball mount that carried either two 40mm anti-aircraft guns, or a single 40mm cannon flanked by a pair of 0.50in machine guns. The performance was not felt to be acceptable, and the project was terminated in October 1944.

T53 90mm gun motor carriage

The T53 90mm gun motor carriage also dated from July 1942 and was intended for anti-aircraft use. An M4 chassis was modified to place the engine at the centre, with a 90mm gun at the rear, although the subsequent T53E1 variant, which was intended for both the anti-aircraft and anti-tank roles, saw the engine moved back to its normal position and the gun placed at the centre. The project was abandoned in May 1944.

Table 4:
Major Sherman adaptations and modifications

Many other upgrades and modifications were made during the post-war years, for example by the armies of Argentina, Chile, Egypt, India and Mexico. In 1980/81, Jane's *Armour and Artillery* directory reported that Shermans were still in service with ten nations, and even as late as 1990 Israeli Military Industries and the US company NAPCO Industries were both still offering power-pack upgrades.

Designation	Date	Origin and/or user(s)	Description
Ambulance tanks			
Ambutank	1967	Israeli Defence Force	Converted M4A3 hulls, with turret removed and engine repositioned for use as front-line ambulance.
Amphibious tanks			
Sherman Belch	1944	British Army	Sherman DD with water spray around canvas wading screen; experimental only.
Sherman DD	1943	British Army	Sherman III or Sherman V with canvas wading screen and twin propeller drive.
Sherman DD	1944	US Army	M4 and M4A1 with canvas wading screen and twin propeller drive.
Sherman DD Mk I	1943	British Army	Sherman III or Sherman V with improved canvas wading screen and twin propeller drive.
Sherman DD Mk II	1943	British Army	Sherman III or Sherman V with improved canvas wading screen and twin propeller drive.
Sherman DD Mk III	1945	US Army, British Army	Sherman III or Sherman IIIAY with improved canvas wading screen and twin propeller drive.
Sherman DD Mk III rocket egress	1945	British Army	Sherman III or Sherman IIIAY with rocket-assistance for climbing steep banks; experimental only.
Sherman DD APC	1944	British Army	Turretless Sherman DD converted to armoured personnel carrier; experimental only.
Sherman Gin-and-it	1945	British Army	Sherman DD with folded mat for traction on mud; experimental only.
Sherman Topee	1944	British Army	Sherman DD with flotation pontoons; experimental only.
T6, M19	1944	US Army	M4A1 with steel floats.
Bridgelayers			
M2 ARK, Sherman ARK	1944	US Army	Armoured ramp carrier.
M4 mobile assault bridge	1944	US Army	M4-based mobile assault bridge.
Sherman ARK Hopper	1944	British Army	Armoured ramp carrier.
Sherman Plymouth	1944	Canadian Army	Bailey bridge launcher.
Sherman Twaby ARK	1944	British Army	Armoured ramp carrier.
SPAB	1955	US Army	Self-propelled assault bridge.
–	1945	US Army	Mobile folding bridge.
Combat engineer vehicles			
M1, M1A1, M4, T7	1943	US Army	Bulldozer, tank mounting.
M4 Doozit	1943	US Army	M4 with M1 dozer blade and T40 rocket-launcher for breaching sea walls, etc; experimental only.
T31	1945	US Army	Demolition tank; M4A3 HVSS with 105mm howitzer and 2 x 7.2in (183mm) rocket tubes; prototype only.

Designation	Date	Origin and/or user(s)	Description
Flame-throwers			
E13-13, E13-R1-13R2, E20-20	1944	US Army	M4A1-based flame-thrower.
E4R2-5R1, E4R3-5R1 (M3-4-3)	1945	US Army	Flame-thrower kit for fitting in place of hull machine gun.
E4R4-4R, E5-6RC	1945	US Army	Flame-thrower kit for fitting in place of hull machine gun.
E6R1, E6R3, E12R3	1945	US Army	Flame-thrower kit for fitting alongside co-driver's periscope.
E7-7	1945	US Army	Flame gun fitted in place of main gun.
M4 Crocodile	1943	US Army	M4-based flame-thrower with jettisonable fuel trailer; British conversion for US Army.
M5-4, M42B1, M42B3	1944	US Army	M4-based flame-thrower with E7 flame gun.
POA	1944	US Army	Flame gun firing through 105mm howitzer tube.
POA-CWS-75-H1	1944	US Army	M4A3-based flame-thrower firing through 75mm gun tube.
POA-CWS-75-H2	1944	US Army	M4A3-based flame-thrower with 75mm gun and co-axial flame gun.
POA-CWS-H5	1945	US Army	M4A3-based flame-thrower with 75mm gun or 105mm howitzer and co-axial flame gun.
Sherman Badger	1945	Canadian Army	Conversion of turretless M4A2 with Wasp flame gun.
Sherman Ronson	1944	British Army	M4-based flame-thrower using Canadian Ronson flame gun.
Sherman Salamander	1944	British Army	M4-based flame-thrower with Wasp flame gun.
Sherman V Adder	1943	British Army	M4A4-based flame-thrower.
T33	1947	US Army	M4A3E2-based flame-thrower with 75mm gun and co-axial flame gun; experimental only.
T68	1953	US Army	M4-based flame-thrower with Canadian Iroquois flame gun.

ABOVE US Army welded-hull Sherman, probably an M4A3, fitted with the M1 bulldozer blade. *(Tank Museum)*

ABOVE RIGHT Between October 1944 and April 1945 about 75 redundant British M4A2s had their turrets and armaments removed and were converted to armoured personnel carriers (APC) to accommodate ten men. The converted vehicle was dubbed the Kangaroo. *(Warehouse Collection)*

RIGHT Israeli Defence Force (IDF) Sherman-based battlefield ambulance. Officially described as a 'medical evacuation tank', the vehicle was fitted with a Cummins diesel engine installed at the front of the hull, leaving space for a medical attendant and four stretchers in the spacious rear compartment. *(Bukvoed)*

Designation	Date	Origin and/or user(s)	Description
Mine-clearing devices			
M1 Dragon	1944	US Army	Mine exploder using a hose filled with liquid explosive; experimental only.
M2 demolition snake	1943	Canadian Army	Mine exploder using a hose filled with liquid explosive.
M4 Snake	1943	US Army	Mine exploder using a hose filled with liquid explosive; experimental only.
Sherman AMRCR	1943	British Army	Anti-mine reconnaissance castor roller.
Sherman Bullshorn	1943	British Army	Mine plough; experimental only.
Sherman CIRD	1944	Canadian Army	Canadian indestructible roller device.
Sherman Conger	1943	British Army	Mine exploder using a hose filled with liquid explosive.
Sherman Crab I	1943	British Army	Flail.
Sherman Crab II	1943	British Army	Flail.
Sherman Jeffries	1943	British Army	Mine plough; experimental only.
Sherman Lobster	1943	British Army	Flail; experimental only.
Sherman Lulu	1944	British Army	Roller with electro-magnetic mine-detection equipment; experimental only.
Sherman Marquis, Octopus	1943	British Army	Flail; experimental only.
Sherman MDI	1943	British Army	Mine plough; experimental only.
Sherman Porcupine	1944	British Army	Spiked mine roller; experimental only.
Sherman Pram Scorpion	1943	British Army	Flail; experimental only.
Sherman Scorpion IV	1943	British Army	Flail; using equipment developed for M3-based Scorpion IV.
Sherman Snake	1943	British Army	Mine exploder using a hose filled with liquid explosive.
Sherman Tapeworm	1943	British Army	Mine exploder using a hose filled with liquid explosive.
T1E1 Earthworm	1943	US Army	Mine roller.
T1E2	1943	US Army	Mine roller; experimental only.
T1E3, M1 Aunt Jemima	1944	US Army	Mine roller.
T1E4, T1E5, T1E6	1944	US Army	Mine exploder; experimental only.
T2	1943	US Army	Flail; as British Crab I.
T2E1	1943	US Army	Mine exploder; experimental only.
T2E2	1943	US Army	Mine plough.
T3, T3E1, T3E2	1945	US Army	Flail; experimental only.
T4 (flail)	1944	US Army	Flail; as British Crab II.
T4 (plough)	1942	US Army	Mine plough; experimental only.
T5, T5E1, T5E2, T5E3	1943	US Army	Mine plough.
T6, T6E1	1943	US Army	Mine plough; experimental only.
T7	1943	US Army	Mine roller; experimental only.
T8 Johnnie Walker	1944	US Army	Mine exploder; experimental only.
T9, T9E1	1944	US Army	Sheeps-foot mine roller; experimental only.
T10	1944	US Army	Remote mine roller; experimental only.
T11, T12, T14	1944	US Army	Mine exploder; experimental only.
T15, T15E1, T15E2	1944	US Army	Mine-resistant vehicle; experimental only.
Miscellaneous			
De-frocked Priest	1944	Canadian Army	Armoured personnel carrier; based on M7 105mm howitzer gun motor carriage chassis.
Eyal	1973	Israeli Defence Force	Observation tank for use in Suez Canal Zone.
M4 APC	–	Israeli Defence Force	Personnel carrier/command vehicle.
M4 with assault sledges	1943	US Army	M4 adapted to tow armoured sledges for assault role; experimental only.
M30	–	US Army	Cargo carrier based on M12 155mm gun motor carriage hull.
Rhinoceros, Prong	1944	US Army, British Army	Spiked device to assist in uprooting hedgerows; also known as the 'Culin hedgerow cutter' after its inventor.
Sherman fascine carrier	1943	British Army	Turretless tank with carrier for fascine bundle, used for ditch crossing.
Sherman gun tractor	–	British Army	Turretless tank used for towing 17-pounder anti-tank gun.
Sherman Kangaroo	1944	Canadian Army	Armoured personnel carrier; based on M4A5 chassis.
Sherman OP	1943	British Army	Observation post, with dummy gun and additional radio equipment.
–	1944	US Army	Loudspeaker mount for psychological operations.
–	1944	US Army	M4A1-based dozer/fire fighter.
–	1944	US Army	Turretless tank for handling radioactive material.
–	1947	US Army	Airfield crash/rescue vehicle.

LEFT Dating from the 1,000-day War of Attrition fought between Israel and Egypt from 1967 to 1970, the Israeli Defence Force (IDF) *Eyal* conversion was described as an 'observation tank'. Just three were constructed with the intention of allowing observers to maintain watch across the elevated banks that had been constructed along the Suez Canal. The example shown here, which is at the IDF armour museum at Latrun, was based on an M4A1 with HVSS suspension. *(Bukvoed)*

BELOW LEFT Not an official variant 1: Sherman M4A4 mounting a tubular-steel superstructure complete with canvas covers intended to make the tank look like a truck from the air. *(Tank Museum)*

BELOW Not an official variant 2: These inflatable rubber tanks were made by the Dunlop Rubber Company and others and used as decoys to confuse enemy aircraft. When deflated, the 'tank' could be packed away in a large bag. *(IWM, H42531)*

Designation	Date	Origin and/or user(s)	Description
–	–	US Army	M4A3-based dozer/fire fighter.
Recovery vehicles			
M34	1944	US Army	Full-track prime mover; as M32B1 but with jib removed.
M74, M74B1	1954	US Army	Upgraded M32 recovery vehicles.
M74	–	Israeli Defence Force	Converted M32 recovery vehicles with M50/M51 modifications.
Sherman BARV	1943	British Army	Beach armoured recovery vehicle.
Sherman II ARV Mk III	1944	British Army	Armoured recovery vehicle; based on M4A1 chassis (as US Army M32B1).
Sherman III ARV Mk I	1944	British Army	Armoured recovery vehicle; based on M4A2 chassis.
Sherman V ARV Mk I	1944	British Army	Armoured recovery vehicle with front and rear jibs and dummy gun; based on M4A4 chassis.
Sherman V ARV Mk II	1944	British Army	Armoured recovery vehicle with front and rear jibs and dummy gun; based on M4A4 chassis.
T5, M32	1943	US Army	Tank recovery vehicle; based on M4 chassis.
T5E1, M32A1B1, M32B1	1944	US Army	Tank recovery vehicle; based on M4A1 chassis.
T5E2, M32A1B2, M32B2	1944	US Army	Tank recovery vehicle; based on M4A2 chassis.
T5E3, M32A1B3, M32B3	1944	US Army	Tank recovery vehicle; based on M4A3 chassis.
T5E4, M32B4	1944	US Army	Tank recovery vehicle; based on M4A4 chassis.
T7	1943	US Army	Tank recovery vehicle; based on M4 chassis; experimental only.

Designation	Date	Origin and/or user(s)	Description
T14	1945	US Army	Tank recovery vehicle; based on M4A3 chassis.
Rocket-launchers			
290mm rocket-launcher	–	Israeli Defence Force	36 x 290mm rockets.
T34 Calliope	1943	US Army	60 x 4.6in (117mm) rocket tubes mounted on frame above turret.
T34E1	1943	US Army	As T34 but with 14 additional tubes.
T34E2	1945	US Army	60 x 7.2in (183mm) rocket tubes in jettisonable mount.
T37, T40, M17 Whizbang	1944	US Army	20 x 7.2in (183mm) rocket tubes in box mount.
T40 (short)	1944	US Army	20 x 7.2in (183mm) rocket tubes in box mount; shorter tubes; experimental only.
T39	–	US Army	20 x 7.2in (183mm) rocket tubes in T2 box mount; experimental only.
T45	1944	US Army	24 x 4.5in (114mm) rocket tubes in barrage launcher.
T64	1944	US Army	20 x 7.2in (183mm) rocket tubes in box mount.
T72	1944	US Army	60 x 4.6in (117mm) rocket tubes mounted on frame above turret; experimental only.
T73	1944	US Army	10 x 7.2in (183mm) rocket tubes in box mount; experimental only.
T76	1944	US Army	M4A1 with 7.5in (190mm) rocket-launcher in place of 75mm gun; experimental only.
T76E1	1944	US Army	M4A3 HVSS with 7.5in (190mm) rocket-launcher in place of 75mm gun; experimental only.
T99	1945	US Army	Multiple rocket-launcher; 22 x 4.5in (114mm) rocket tubes in each of two turret side mounts.
T105	1944	US Army	M4A1 with 7.5in (190mm) rocket-launcher in place of 75mm gun; experimental only.
–	–	US Army	M4A3 with 60 x 4.5in (114mm) rocket tubes.
Searchlight tanks			
M4 CDL	1944	British Army	Canal defence light with 75mm M3 gun and co-axial searchlight.
M4 Leaflet or 'E' vehicle	1944	US Army	Night fighting tank with 75mm M3 gun and co-axial searchlight.
T10E1 shop tractor	1944	US Army	Canal defence light with 75mm M3 gun and co-axial searchlight; British conversion for US Army.
T52 searchlight	1950	US Army	Searchlight tank on M4A3 chassis.
Self-propelled anti-aircraft guns			
Skink	1944	Canadian Army	20mm quad anti-aircraft tank; 4 x 20mm Hispano Suiza or Polsten cannon.
T52	1942	US Army	Multiple gun motor carriage; 1 x 40mm gun, 2 x 0.50in machine guns; experimental only.
T53, T53E1	1942	US Army	90mm gun motor carriage; experimental only.
Self-propelled gun mounts			
L33, L39 Ro'em	1981	Israeli Defence Force	155mm self-propelled gun on IDF M50 chassis (Soltam M-68 155mm howitzer).
M7 (9.75in mortar)	1945	US Army	M7 9.75in mortar motor carriage; M7 howitzer with 105mm gun replaced by 0.75in mortar; experimental only.
M7B1	1944	US Army	105mm howitzer motor carriage; known as Priest by the British.
M7B2	1951	US Army	105mm howitzer motor carriage.
M43	1945	US Army	8in gun motor carriage.
M50	1962	Israeli Defence Force	155mm self-propelled gun on IDF M50 chassis.
Sexton	1943	British Army, Canadian Army	25-pounder self-propelled gun.
T51	1943	US Army	25-pounder gun motor carriage.
T52	1942	US Army	Multiple gun motor carriage; 1 x or 2 x 40mm AA guns plus 2 x 0.50in machine guns in ball-mount.
T53, T53E1	1942	US Army	90mm gun motor carriage; 90mm AA gun mounted at rear of chassis.
T83, M12, M40	1944	US Army	155mm gun motor carriage.
T89	1945	US Army	8in howitzer motor carriage.
T94	-	US Army	10in/250mm mortar motor carriage; experimental only.
Tank destroyers			
Achilles IIC	1943	British Army	17-pounder self-propelled gun; M10 rearmed with British 17-pounder Mk V gun.
T24, T40, M9	1941	US Army	3in gun motor carriage.
T35, T35E1, M10, M10A1	1942	US Army, British Army	3in gun motor carriage.
T70, T72	1943	US Army	76mm gun motor carriage; experimental only.
T71, M36, M36B1	1944	US Army	90mm gun motor carriage.
T71E1, M36B2	1945	US Army	90mm gun motor carriage.

'One of the most remarkable achievements of the automobile industry has been in the tank field. It was a product of which they knew nothing...(and) if ever the ingenuity of the industry met its test it has been on this job.'

Detroit Times, 1942

Chapter Three

Building the Sherman

Henry Ford's mass production techniques revolutionised the motor industry, gradually reducing the time required to construct a Model T from 14 hours to 1 hour 33 minutes. By the time the USA entered World War Two in 1941 mass production techniques had become the norm, and it seemed entirely logical that tanks should also be produced in this way. Between 1942 and 1945, ten US companies – three of which also constructed brand-new manufacturing facilities – and one Canadian produced 49,422 Sherman tanks. By contrast, total German tank production between the years 1940 and 1945 totalled just 24,360 units.

OPPOSITE Simultaneous facing and drilling of a turret casting at the Fisher Tank Grand Blanc facility. *(Warehouse Collection)*

ABOVE Brand-new
GM diesel-engined
M4A2 photographed
at Fisher Tank Grand
Blanc; note the twin
fixed machine guns
in the bow, fitted only
to early production
examples. *(Warehouse
Collection)*

Production

Like any motor vehicle, a tank is an assembly of parts from literally dozens of manufacturers, and, in a general way, tank building followed the processes already established for motor car production, with components produced in various separate plants and then brought together for assembly at a number of prime locations. Eleven prime companies are credited with having built Shermans, with contributions coming from across the US automotive and engineering industries.

For example, face-hardened steel plate initially came from two safe manufacturers – Diebold Safe & Lock Company and The Mosler Safe Company – with additional material subsequently coming from Gary Armor, Republic Steel, Henry Disston, and Carnegie-Illinois. Steel hull and turret castings were supplied by almost 40 different manufacturers, the major contributors being American Steel Foundries, Columbia Steel Company, Continental Foundry and Machine Company, General Steel Castings Corporation (which had produced the first ever one-piece cast upper

tank hull in 1939), Pittsburgh Steel Foundry Corporation, and Union Steel Castings. Whilst most of these companies were able to expand their existing casting and foundry facilities with the aid of financing from the US government's Defense Plant Corporation, the Ford Motor Company actually constructed a brand new foundry with the capacity to produce 10,000 tons per month.

Ford, Chrysler, and General Motors all supplied their own engines, whilst other power units came from Caterpillar, Wright and Continental. Transmissions were produced by Detroit Tank Arsenal, both for its own use and for others, whilst other suppliers included the Buick Division of General Motors, the Caterpillar Tractor Company, the Ford Motor Company, and Reed Roller Bit Company.

In theory all US tank production was subject to test procedures during and on completion of the manufacturing process, and each vehicle was supposedly signed-off by Ordnance Department inspection officials. However, it quickly became apparent that the complexity of the vehicles made the task all but impossible and the test procedures were

simplified, with the manufacturers 'trusted' to produce acceptable materiel. A functional test was conducted on every completed vehicle by staff employed by the manufacturer under the supervision of inspectors from the Ordnance Department. In addition a random number of vehicles were selected from the production line and subjected to 'inspection control testing' at one of the Ordnance proving grounds.

Contracts and serial numbers

The first contracts for the manufacture of Sherman tanks were issued by the British Ministry of Supply (MoS), almost certainly through the offices of the US Ordnance Board. After the introduction of the Lend-Lease Act all contracts for the M4 tank, regardless of end user, originated with the Ordnance Board and were placed directly with the relevant manufacturers, generally with a single contract on which the quantities were varied as time went on. The prices varied considerably according to the supplier, the date, and the variant in question. For example, in 1945, the basic 75mm

ABOVE The M4 was constructed by American Locomotive, Baldwin Locomotive, Detroit Tank Arsenal, Pullman-Standard and the Pressed Steel Car Company. The example shown here, which dates from 1943, is one of 841 examples fitted both with horizontal volute spring suspension and the 105mm howitzer. *(Tank Museum)*

BELOW Every tank to be completed was subjected to a functional test conducted by staff employed by the manufacturer under the supervision of inspectors from the Ordnance Department. A random number of vehicles were also selected from the production line and subjected to 'inspection control testing' at one of the Ordnance proving grounds. *(Tank Museum)*

M4 with the vertical volute suspension system (VVSS) cost $49,173, the M4A3E2 was priced at $56,812, and the Caterpillar-engined M4A6 was $64,455; the average 1945 price for a Sherman was $49,793.

The serial numbers and US Army registration numbers were also assigned by the Ordnance Board: the serial number appeared on the data plate, and was also often stamped on to the hull itself, whilst the registration number was painted on the side of the hull. The numbers were generally assigned in blocks, but because some manufacturers were constructing more than one variant there is not necessarily any direct correlation between serial number and registration number. See Table 14, page 156.

Tank manufacturers

The companies credited with constructing Sherman tanks are American Locomotive, Baldwin Locomotive, Detroit Tank Arsenal (Chrysler Corporation), Federal Machine & Welder, Fisher Tank Grand Blanc (General Motors Corporation), Ford Motor Company, Lima Locomotive, Pacific Car & Foundry, the Pressed Steel Car Company, and Pullman-

Standard in the USA; and the Canadian Montreal Locomotive Works. The largest number came from Fisher Tank Grand Blanc and Detroit Tank Arsenal, with production totals of 11,358 and 17,947, respectively... no wonder that General Campbell was able tell the men – and women, since the number of men sent to the front saw an increase in the employment of women in US war production – of the Detroit Tank Arsenal that 'the more than 20,000 tanks you have turned out in four years have played a key part in shifting the tide of war'. It has been claimed that at the height of production, one M4 Sherman rolled out of a US factory every 30 minutes.

After manufacture, the tanks were generally shipped to one of the Ordnance Department tank depots, where any required modifications were made and the tanks were stored until required for issue. These depots were also responsible for preparing the tanks for shipment overseas. The first tank depot was opened in January 1942 at the New York Central Railroad workshops at Toledo, Ohio, and was run by the Electric Auto-Lite Company. Further depots were opened by the Ford Motor Company at Chester, Pennsylvania, and Richmond,

BELOW The first M4s to be produced were the cast-hull M4A1s with a 75mm gun, manufactured at the Lima Locomotive Works in Ohio.
(Warehouse Collection)

California, and a fourth depot was opened at an abandoned gun plant at Lima, Ohio, which eventually took over the operation previously located at Toledo.

Manufacturing shortages often meant that tanks were shipped to the depots without tools, equipment or supplies. Tracks proved a particular problem in 1942. The following year a ban was introduced which forbade manufacturers from shipping tanks which were not fully equipped, and the number of shortages per vehicle was reduced from an average of 40 to around three.

American Locomotive Company

The American Locomotive Company (ALCO) was formed in 1901 by the merger of eight smaller companies, and was headquartered in Schenectady, New York. Three years after its formation, ALCO acquired control of the Montreal-based Locomotive and Machine Company, renaming it as the Montreal Locomotive Works (MLW). Following the acquisition of MLW, all of the plants, except those at Schenectady and Montreal, were closed and the company went on to become one of the largest producers of railway locomotives in the USA.

The equipment which was installed

ABOVE Turret, complete with the turret basket that provided a floor, being lowered onto a completed M4A1 hull at Lima Locomotive Works. (Warehouse Collection)

LEFT Lima Locomotive Works constructed a total of 1,605 M4A1s, but the type was also built by Pressed Steel and Pacific Car & Foundry. A total of 9,707 examples was produced, 3,426 of which were fitted with the 76mm weapon as shown here. (Warehouse Collection)

at ALCO's Schenectady plant for lifting, cutting, shaping and manipulating the heavy components used in locomotive production made the company an ideal choice for producing tanks, and in February 1942 it started constructing M3A1 medium tanks alongside its existing locomotive production areas. The tanks were assembled on a production-line basis, with seven major assembly stations where components were added to the lower hull. In September 1942 ALCO switched to producing the M4 Sherman, producing 2,150 examples of the M4 between February and December 1943, and just 150 of the M4A2 between September 1942 and April 1943. At the end of 1943 the company ceased tank production in favour of much-needed locomotives, going on to produce 1,086 steam locomotives and 157 diesel-electric locomotives for the US War Department.

Between 1940 and 1945 ALCO produced a total of 2,985 tanks, 3.7% of the total US tank production during this period. Production of locomotives in Schenectady ended in 1969.

Baldwin Locomotive Works

Located in Philadelphia, in the state of Pennsylvania, the Baldwin Locomotive Works produced its first railway locomotive in 1832, basing it on an imported engine from Britain.

Five years later the company was turning out 40 locomotives a year. Hard times followed, but the railroad boom of the 1850s saw production rise to new levels.

The company received an order for ten M2A4 light tanks in 1939, and went on to construct hundreds of examples of both the M3 light tank and the M3 medium for the US Ordnance Department and the British Ministry of Supply. Production of the M4A2 Sherman started in October 1942, continuing until November of that year; production of the M4 started in January 1943 and continued until January 1944.

Total tank production at Baldwin's Philadelphia plant was 2,515, of which 1,233 examples were M4s and 12 were M4A2s. Baldwin ceased production of locomotives in 1956 and closed in 1972.

Detroit Tank Arsenal

The Detroit Tank Arsenal – sometimes described as the Detroit Arsenal Tank Plant or DATP – was constructed during 1940/41 by the Chrysler Corporation on a 113-acre (0.46-hectare) site, formerly farmland, at Warren, Michigan, a suburb of Detroit. More than 1,000 machine tools were installed in the plant, together with 8,500 specially designed jigs, and it was the first such facility in the USA intended

BELOW Lowering the massive Chrysler A-57 multi-bank engine into the M4A4 hull at Detroit Tank Arsenal. *(Warehouse Collection)*

BELOW RIGHT Sherman assembly line at Detroit Tank Arsenal. *(Warehouse Collection)*

for the mass production of tanks, producing 22,234 vehicles and refurbishing a further 2,825 between 1940 and 1945 – more than 25% of US tank production. Of this total, some 17,947 were of the M4 medium design.

Although the plant was originally contracted to build the M2A1 light tank at a rate of 100 tanks a month, this contract was cancelled in favour of the M3 medium, production of which started with two pilot models in April 1941. By 10 July 1942 the facility had constructed a total of 3,100 M3 tanks, before production was switched to the M4 Sherman, the first example of which rolled off the line on 22 July. By 3 August, 21 days after the switchover began, the M3 had been superseded completely by the M4, and the Detroit Arsenal went on to produce examples of the M4, M4A3, M4A4 and M4A6. At the peak of production in June 1944 there were five assembly lines constructing Shermans, with additional machining work on sub-components carried out at other Chrysler factories.

During 1943/44 some 1,610 older Shermans, destined for various Allies under the Lend-Lease arrangements, were also refurbished at the Detroit Tank Arsenal.

The last Shermans were produced at the Detroit Arsenal in 1945, but tank production continued at the site under the US Ordnance Department until May 1952, when Chrysler resumed control. As a so-called 'government-owned, contractor-operated' (GOCO) facility, it was operated by Chrysler Defense Division for the government until March 1982, when Chrysler sold the Defense Division to General Dynamics Land Systems. The plant was closed in 1996.

ABOVE LEFT Attaching the suspension units to the hull. *(Warehouse Collection)*

ABOVE View of the spray shop at Detroit Tank Arsenal; it's interesting to see how the sprayers are actually standing on the hull that they are painting rather than working from an access gantry. *(Warehouse Collection)*

BELOW Fitting the turret at Detroit Tank Arsenal; the turret weighed five tons and this was amongst the last operations to be completed. Note the bolted three-piece differential housing. *(Warehouse Collection)*

Federal Machine & Welder Company

Established at around the beginning of the 20th century in Warren, Ohio, the Federal Machine & Welder Company was a manufacturer of electrical equipment. The company produced 540 M4A2 tanks between December 1942 and December 1943, as well as 400 M32B1 armoured recovery vehicles. In April 1944 the company started a refurbishment programme, rebuilding 317 M4A2 tanks for Lend-Lease, the last being completed in November of that year.

Fisher Tank Grand Blanc

Established in 1941/42 at a cost of $37 million, and with a maximum production capacity of 1,000 M4 medium tanks a month, the Fisher Tank Arsenal was located at Grand Blanc, Michigan, just south of Flint, and was operated by the Fisher Body Division of General Motors Corporation. Initial discussions with the US Ordnance Board concerning the establishment of the plant had taken place in September 1941 and it was authorised in February 1942. The first tank, an M4A2, was delivered in March 1942, preparations having taken place at the GM Fisher Flint Division whilst the new plant

BELOW Impressive line-up of hulls and turrets at Detroit Tank Arsenal. Note that there is a mix of welded and composite hulls evident.
(Warehouse Collection)

was being constructed. By August 1942, the plant had constructed 205 Shermans, and by the end of the war 13,137 tanks had been produced, of which some 11,358 were of the M4A2 and M4A3 design. Although, at $67,173 per tank, the initial contract price was high, the Fisher facility eventually proved to be one of the lowest-cost producers in the programme. Production of the M4A2 continued until October 1944, whilst the M4A3 was produced during 1944 and 1945. A total of 218 older Shermans were also refurbished at Fisher Tank Grand Blanc during 1944.

In 1947 the Buick Motor Division leased the plant, and it was purchased by Fisher Body in 1951 after tank production ended. Occasionally still referred to as 'the tank plant', the facility was transferred to Buick/Oldsmobile/Chevrolet (BOC) in 1984 and subsequently to the newly formed Cadillac/Luxury Car Division. The site is now described as the Metal Fabrication Division, Grand Blanc Weld Tool Center, and serves as a corporation-wide weld tooling centre.

Ford Motor Company

The Ford Motor Company built 1,690 examples of the M4A3 at their Highland Park Plant, although many of the parts were actually made at the more modern Rouge River Plant. Highland Park had been opened in 1910 and included offices, assembly halls, a generating station and a foundry – this was the site used by Ford to construct the iconic Model T, and which in 1913 became the first automotive plant in the world to adopt a moving production line. Motor car production moved to the new Rouge River Plant in the 1920s, and Highland Park was turned over to the assembly of tractors and the production of trim components until it became one of the sites used by Ford for defence work. The first Ford-built M4A3 was completed in late May 1942, with production ending in the final quarter of 1943 when Ford left the tank production programme to concentrate on other defence equipment.

Ford also established and ran two tank depots on behalf of the Ordnance Department at the company's sites at Richmond, California, and Chester, Pennsylvania.

In 1952 Ford tank production was moved to a new plant at Livonia, Michigan, that had been

BELOW View of the massive rotator jig used at Fisher Tank Grand Blanc to position the hull of the M4A2 for welding. Weighing 37 tons, these rotators were the largest fixtures used for this purpose. *(Warehouse Collection)*

specifically built to produce M48 medium tanks. The Highland Park Plant was given National Monument status in 1978 and is currently used as a storage facility for documents and artefacts for the Henry Ford Museum.

Lima Locomotive Works

Based in the town of Lima, Ohio, the Lima Locomotive Works can trace its origins back to 1878, when James Alley contracted the Lima Machine Works to build a steam locomotive. By 1882 locomotives had become the main product of the Lima Machine Works, and in 1892 the company was reorganised as the Lima Locomotive & Machine Company, later to become known simply as Lima Locomotive Corporation and then as Lima Locomotive Works.

Lima Locomotive was the first company to produce the M4 Sherman in quantity, in the guise of the M4A1, on an assembly line established under a British Ministry of Supply contract. Production started in February 1942, continuing until September 1943, by which time

the company had built 1,655 M4A1 variants and refurbished a further 60.

In 1947 the firm merged with General Machinery Corporation of Hamilton, Ohio, to become Lima-Hamilton. The original Lima factory was closed in 1980.

Montreal Locomotive Works

Established in 1883, the Locomotive & Machine Company of Montreal Limited was Canada's largest producer of steam locomotives, and was purchased by ALCO in 1904 and renamed Montreal Locomotive Works (MLW) some years later. The company prospered during the years following the end of World War One as the Canadian National Railway was modernised.

A total of 188 M4A5 Grizzly tanks were constructed at MLW. The specification was issued in September 1942, and work started in August 1943 on the production line which had been built for the M3-based Canadian Ram II tank. The last Grizzly was produced in December 1943, but the company also refurbished 400 M4A3s, completing these by April 1945.

In 1975, the Quebec-based Bombardier company purchased a majority stake in MLW, eventually leading to a full merger. Bombardier abandoned the production of locomotives in 1985 and the now-unwanted plant was sold to General Electric three years later. It was closed in 1993.

Pacific Car & Foundry Company

The origins of Pacific Car & Foundry can be traced back to 1901, when William Pigott established the Railway Steel & Supply Company, producing rails, railway supplies, iron and steel, and coke. Before long the company was also producing logging trucks for railway use. In 1905 William Pigott established the Seattle Car Manufacturing Company, taking over the truck-building business, inventory and machinery of Railway Steel. Construction of a new factory, at Renton, Washington, began in 1907, and following a fire at the Seattle plant and a period in voluntary receivership the company gradually became well established. In August 1917 the company merged with the Twohy Brothers Company of Portland, and was renamed the Pacific Car & Foundry Company.

Although the company continued to trade as Pacific Car & Foundry, by 1924 it had become a wholly-owned subsidiary of American Car & Foundry.

Production of the M4A1 started at Renton in 1942. A pilot model was completed in May of that year, and the last of 926 tanks rolled off the production line in November 1943. To facilitate production the company enlarged an existing foundry, which enabled it to produce its own armour.

In 1945 Pacific Car & Foundry moved into the truck business following the acquisition of the Kenworth Motor Truck Corporation. In 1972 the company's name was changed to PACCAR and the Renton plant started to specialise in refrigerated railcars.

Pressed Steel Car Company

With its headquarters in New Jersey, the Pressed Steel Car Company was established in February 1899 through the amalgamation of the earlier Schoen Pressed Steel Company and the Fox Solid Pressed Steel Company. Plants were operated in Pittsburgh, Pennsylvania, and in Joliet, Illinois, with the intention of manufacturing 'passenger, freight and street railway cars', and to produce 'trucks, wheels, and other parts of cars'.

Pressed Steel started forging 75mm shells in 1940, before becoming involved in the M3 medium tank project. In March 1942 it became the second company to start producing the M4 tank, and by December 1943 – when their production run ended – the company had produced 8,147 M4, M4A1 and M4A2 tanks.

In 1956, Pressed Steel was bought by US Steel.

Pullman-Standard Car Manufacturing Company

In 1862 George Pullman designed a railway sleeper car with foldaway upper berths. Before long the Pullman Palace Car Company was building and operating luxury sleeping cars across the US railway network. George Pullman died in 1897 and the company was renamed the Pullman Company on 1 January 1900, eventually becoming a household name. In 1930, at the height of the recession, Pullman acquired the Standard Steel Car Company of Hammond, Indiana, renaming the merged entity as the Pullman-Standard Car Manufacturing Company.

In early 1940 Pullman-Standard started to produce 81mm mortars and 75mm shells for the US Army, eventually becoming involved in production of the M3 medium tank, before switching to the M4 Sherman in May 1941. The company constructed both M4 and M4A2 tanks, with a total of 3,426 examples built before production ceased in September 1943.

At the end of the war the company resumed the manufacture of railcars, but production ceased in 1987 when Pullman-Standard was absorbed by Bombardier.

Refurbishment and remanufacture

Between December 1943 and April/May 1945, large numbers of early Shermans which had been retained in the States and had been heavily used as training vehicles for US Army tank crews, were submitted to a programme of remanufacture, refurbishment

Table 5: Manufacturers and refurbishers of M4 Sherman

Company	Variants and numbers constructed/refurbished:												
	M4		M4A1		M4A2		M4A3			M4A3E2	M4A4	M4A5	M4A6
	75mm	105mm	75mm	76mm	75mm	76mm	75mm	76mm	105mm	75mm	75mm	75mm	75mm
Original manufacture													
American Locomotive	2,150	–	–	–	150	–	–	–	–	–	–	–	–
Baldwin Locomotive	1,233	–	–	–	12	–	–	–	–	–	–	–	–
Chrysler (Detroit Arsenal)	1,676	1,641	–	–	–	–	–	4,017	3,039	–	7,499	–	75
Federal Machine & Welder	–	–	–	–	540	–	–	–	–	–	–	–	–
GM (Fisher Tank Grand Blanc)	–	–	–	–	4,614	2,894	3,071	525	–	254	–	–	–
Ford Motor Company	–	–	–	–	–	–	1,690	–	–	–	–	–	–
Lima Locomotive Works	–	–	1,655	–	–	–	–	–	–	–	–	–	–
Montreal Locomotive Works	–	–	–	–	–	–	–	–	–	–	–	188	–
Pacific Car & Foundry	–	–	926	–	–	–	–	–	–	–	–	–	–
Pressed Steel	1,000	–	3,700	3,426	–	21	–	–	–	–	–	–	–
Pullman-Standard	689	–	–	–	2,737	–	–	–	–	–	–	–	–
Sub-totals	*6,748*	*1,641*	*6,281*	*3,426*	*8,053*	*2,915*	*4,761*	*4,542*	*3,039*	*254*	*7,499*	*188*	*75*
Total by variant	**8,389**	**–**	**9,707**	**–**	**10,968**	**–**	**12,596**	**–**	**–**	**–**	**7,687**	**–**	**75**
Grand total of Sherman production: USA 49,234; Canada 188													
Refurbishment*													
Chrysler, Evansville plant	446	–	1,216	–	–	–	–	–	–	–	–	–	–
Chrysler, Detroit Arsenal	1,610	–	–	–	–	–	–	–	–	–	–	–	–
Federal Machine & Welder	–	–	–	–	317	–	–	–	–	–	–	–	–
GM (Fisher Tank Grand Blanc)	–	–	–	–	218	–	–	–	–	–	–	–	–
IH Quad Cities Tank Arsenal	289	–	737	–	–	–	–	–	–	–	–	–	–
Montreal Locomotive Works	–	–	–	–	–	–	400	–	–	–	–	–	–
US Army Tank Depots	60	–	306	–	–	–	28	–	–	–	–	–	–
Grand total of Sherman refurbishment: 5,880													

* No breakdown available to indicate gun types for refurbished tanks.

and modernisation, designed to render them fit for further service. A total of 5,880 tanks were treated, being stripped down to their component parts and then reassembled using such new parts as were necessary. At the same time, although most retained the original vertical volute spring suspension system (VVSS), many of the late production features were incorporated, including *appliqué* armour on the turret, hull sides and in front of the driver's hood.

Many of these remanufactured vehicles were shipped to Europe to make good the large numbers of tanks destroyed during the Battle of the Bulge in the winter of 1944/45. During this six-week action some 840,000 Allied troops with 1,300 US medium tanks had been pitched against 200–500,000 Germans with perhaps 1,800 tanks, and the US Army had seen 800 of its tanks destroyed.

BELOW Battle-weary tanks were rebuilt by both US and British Army workshops – this M4A4, photographed in a British REME workshop, is having the turret refitted; note that the front drive sprockets have also been removed. *(Tank Museum)*

Engine manufacturers

Seven different types of engine were used in the Sherman tank, with varying degrees of success, being produced by Wright, Continental, General Motors, Chrysler Corporation, Ford, and Caterpillar. Although there was little similarity between the various engine types, the users often described the variants in the most basic way, referring simply to 'diesel Shermans' and 'petrol Shermans', presumably as a way of avoiding being placed in the position of having to operate both types simultaneously.

Caterpillar Tractor

The M4E1 and the production M4A6 used a Caterpillar D-200A radial diesel multi-fuel engine that was effectively a conversion of the Wright G-200 Cyclone 9; the engine was later designated the RD-1820 by the Ordnance Board. The development work was carried out by the Caterpillar Tractor Company of Peoria, Illinois, the same company also being contracted to build the production engines.

General Motors

All M4A2 variants were powered by the General Motors Detroit Diesel 6046D twin diesel power unit, consisting essentially of a pair of six-cylinder 6-71 two-stroke diesel engines installed side by side, geared together, and coupled to a common propeller shaft. Since the early 1930s GM had been striving to develop practical, lightweight, powerful and fast two- and four-cycle diesel engines that could replace steam in the locomotive industry, and the Detroit Diesel Division was established in 1937/38, with premises at West Outer Drive, Detroit, to research, develop and promote smaller diesel engines for marine and industrial use.

Ford Motor Company

The M4A3 was powered by the Ford GAA V8, a massive double overhead-cam petrol engine that was derived from an earlier experimental Ford aircraft engine – which Henry Ford is said to have designed when he failed to secure a licence to build the Rolls-Royce Merlin engine. At 18,026cc (1,100in^3), these engines are reputed to be the largest aluminium engines ever built, and were constructed at Ford's Lincoln Plant at 6,200 West Warren Avenue, Detroit. As well as being put into the Ford-built M4A3, thousands of these power units were also supplied to the Detroit Tank Arsenal and Fisher Tank Grand Blanc, both of which were also constructing the M4A3.

Chrysler Corporation

Most unusual of the Sherman engines was the Chrysler A-57 multi-bank, a massive 30-cylinder composite petrol engine developed in considerable haste from a standard six-cylinder motor car engine and put into production at Chrysler's Jefferson Avenue plant, Detroit, in the spring of 1942. At 370bhp net the power output was not up to the levels of the Ford GAA, and in service the A-57 proved to be the least reliable of the US tank engines. The Ordnance Board recommended that it be discontinued from production once a sufficient number of other, more satisfactory, power plants became available.

Wright and Continental

The M4, M4A1 and M4A5 Grizzly were fitted with a Wright R-975 Whirlwind nine-cylinder radial petrol engine, originally designated the J-6 Whirlwind Nine, or J-6-9, and constructed by the Wright Aeronautical Division of the Curtiss-Wright Corporation, based in New Jersey. The R-975 remained in production until 1945, by which time some 7,000 had been produced. A further 53,000 examples were constructed under licence by the Continental Aircraft Engine Company of Mobile, Alabama, with production established in a rehabilitated Continental Motors plant in Detroit. Continental continued to produce these units into the 1950s.

Tank guns

The 75mm tank M2 and M3 guns were developed by the US Bureau of Ordnance, and were originally produced by Watervliet Arsenal in New York State – 1,000 of the 1,200 guns required for the M3 Lee/Grant medium tank came from this source during 1941, but with the introduction of the M4 Sherman the requirement for the weapon increased, and some 26,000 were called for during 1942 alone.

LEFT Seven types of engine were used in the Sherman, with examples constructed by Caterpillar, Chrysler, Continental, GM Detroit Diesel, Ford Motor Company and Wright; the photograph shows the Ford GAA V8 petrol engine, the only engine to be produced in volume that was purpose-designed for use in tanks. *(Warehouse Collection)*

At this stage other companies became involved, including the Empire Ordnance Corporation of Philadelphia, the Cowdrey Machine Works, based in Fitchburg, Massachusetts, and the Oldsmobile Division of General Motors.

The 75mm gun was replaced in production by the 76mm M1 in 1944.

Lend-Lease

Having been drawn into World War One somewhat against its will, the USA was keen to remain uninvolved in what was seen as yet another European conflict. Even before Hitler's intentions towards his neighbours had become clear, between 1935 and 1939 the USA had passed four neutrality acts designed to prevent belligerent nations from conducting war on their neighbours using materiel supplied from the USA, and to prevent the nation from being drawn into any such conflicts.

The first of these acts banned all arms and ammunition shipments to belligerent nations, and placed America's armaments industry under federal control for six months through the mechanism of the National Munitions Control Board, which monitored companies involved in defence work. However, in 1937 President Franklin D. Roosevelt's Neutrality Act 1937 lifted the embargo for a period of two years to allow nations that were at war to buy military items from the USA on a strict 'cash-and-carry' basis. In March 1939, after Germany invaded Czechoslovakia, Roosevelt sought to further revise or eliminate the neutrality legislation and

successfully lobbied Congress to repeal the mandatory arms embargo.

This meant that in 1940 American industry was able to supply Britain with guns, tanks and trucks, providing they were paid for up front and shipped at Britain's expense. It wasn't all 'cash-and-carry', however, and in September 1940 the USA supplied 50 ageing destroyers to Britain in return for bases in the West Indies and South America, and at the same time Britain allowed the USA to take over air and naval bases in Bermuda and Newfoundland. But during the 16 months that had followed the British declaration of war on Germany, Britain had spent $4.5 billion on war supplies, virtually exhausting the Treasury's gold and dollar reserves, and putting itself in the position of being unable to pay American industry for the goods that were being supplied. By January 1941 few new British contracts were being placed in the USA, and, desperate for a lifeline, but equally desperate for money, Churchill went 'cap in hand' to the American government for assistance. Roosevelt was reluctant to believe that the once mighty British Empire was strapped for cash, and it wasn't until Churchill ordered Treasury officials to

effectively open the books to the Americans that Roosevelt was persuaded that if Britain was to continue to hold Hitler's forces at bay, then the USA had to extend some form of credit to its transatlantic ally.

Neither Congress nor the American public was happy about this ... but, despite his reluctance to allow the USA to be drawn into another European conflict, Roosevelt was nervous of Hitler's intentions. He believed that if Britain were given financial assistance then the war in Europe might be of shorter duration and that it would be less likely that US troops would become involved. His dilemma was how to 'sell' to Congress and the American taxpayer the idea of giving credit to Britain. He had to come up with a way of providing aid to Britain that did not involve the use of the words 'loan', 'credit' or 'subsidy', and by the end of December was asking his cabinet to devise a solution to the problem. One of his advisers, Harold L. Ickes, used an analogy that explained the situation well, saying that 'We Americans are like the householder who refuses to lend or sell his fire extinguisher to help put out the fire in the house that is right next door.' On 17 December, at a presidential press conference, Roosevelt invoked Ickes's fire extinguisher analogy – 'What do I do in such a crisis,' he asked. 'I don't say... "neighbor, my garden hose cost me $15; you have to pay me $15 for it"... I don't want $15... I want my garden hose back after the fire is over. And if the hose were to be damaged during the fight then the neighbor would be under a "gentleman's obligation to repay in kind", without any need for an invoice.'

Using this analogy, Roosevelt proposed that the USA would be prepared to 'lend' military materiel to Britain, and ultimately to others, and that by this means the USA would become 'the arsenal of democracy'. On 11 March 1941 the Lend-Lease Bill was passed into law, giving Roosevelt the power to 'sell, transfer, exchange, or lend equipment, including weapons, or other equipment, to any country to help it defend itself against the Axis powers' – with the President himself to set the terms for aid. The very next day, Congress was asked to appropriate $7 billion to start producing planes, tanks, guns and food for Britain and the Empire, and for China; the USSR was included in November 1941.

The Act, which was extended in March 1943, enabled the industrial base of the USA to produce and supply hundreds of thousands of tons of military materiel to America's wartime allies. Well-versed in mass-production techniques and safe from German bombing raids, the US automotive industry turned out millions of rugged, reliable trucks and the parts to keep them running, whilst the erstwhile builders of railway locomotives turned their hand to producing tanks. The terms of the agreement provided that the material was to be used until time for their return or destruction, which meant that there would be no huge residue of war debts when the conflict was over.

During the conflict, US factories produced 88,410 tanks, most of them of the M4 Sherman pattern, and self-propelled guns, 257,390 artillery pieces, 2,382,311 trucks and motor vehicles, 105,055 mortars, and 2,679,840 machine guns. Although more than 85% of the USA's total war production went to the domestic armed services, Lend-Lease continued until the end of the war, and by 1945 the USA had supplied somewhere between $42 and $50 billion in military goods, oil and fuel, industrial production, food, medical aid and technical services to the Allies. More than $3.5 billion (8.4%) of the total figure came in the form of tanks and armoured fighting vehicles, with a further $2 billion, some 4.9% of the total, supplied as motor vehicles and parts. In 1942 1,110 Shermans were supplied to Britain (including the British Commonwealth), France and the USSR under the Lend-Lease arrangements, but by the following year the figure had risen to 11,947 tanks, and by 1945 the total number of Shermans supplied to the Allies was 22,138, of which 17,184 went to Britain and the British Empire.

It should be no surprise that Britain and the British Empire, including Canada, Australia and New Zealand, were the major beneficiaries of the Lend-Lease scheme, receiving more than 50% of the total. However, large quantities of Lend-Lease goods also went to the Soviet Union, France and China. In all almost 404 nations benefited from the programme.

No charge was made for the Lend-Lease aid delivered during the war, and much of the equipment was effectively supplied as a gift and was never paid for. When the termination of Lend-Lease was announced by Harry S. Truman on 21 August 1945 the American government indicated that it expected some durable goods, such as ships, should be returned, but many believed that calling for the return of other 'Lend-Leased' goods would hurt US domestic manufacturing as the market became flooded with surplus trucks and materiel. The administration elected to charge the Allies for such equipment as remained in service, or was in transit, usually at a 90% discount. Britain, which retained considerable quantities of American-made equipment, was extended a loan to the value of £1.075 billion, with payment to be made across a 50-year period, starting in 1951, at 2% interest.

Lend-Lease was a huge success. It did not keep the USA out of the war – the attack on Pearl Harbor put paid to that idea – but it ensured that American tanks and trucks became a familiar sight wherever the Allies were fighting. In 1945 these vehicles went on to provide the backbone of the armies of the newly-liberated European nations.

'There were five different models of the Sherman tank in production in the USA by the end of 1942. The essential differences were in the engines ... [but] the armament of the M4 tanks introduced further complications.'

US Army in World War II: the Ordnance Department: procurement and supply

Chapter Four

Anatomy of the Sherman

Few would argue that the Sherman was ever at the cutting edge of tank design. Lacking adequate firepower and insufficiently armoured, it presented an attractively tall silhouette and tended to catch fire when hit. However, to dismiss the Sherman in this way does it a disservice. The simplicity of its design made it easy to manufacture and reliable, and its relatively compact size enhanced its manoeuvrability. Whilst General Patton was not being entirely truthful when he said 'the great mobility of the fleet-footed Sherman enables it to evade the slow and unwieldy Tiger', he did have a point.

OPPOSITE Devoid of paint, this welded-hull M4A4 shows how the three-piece differential housing used on all M4A4s is bolted to the hull; note also how the frontal armour is fabricated from a mix of castings and rolled plate. This is a late-pattern hull lacking the direct-vision apertures for the driver and co-driver/bow machine gunner. (Warehouse Collection)

U S Army Technical Manual TM 9-7018 summed up the design of the Sherman by simply stating that it is 'an armored, fulltrack vehicle that mounts one of the following weapons: 75mm gun, 76mm gun, or 105mm howitzer. The vehicle contains a crew compartment in the front and an engine compartment in the rear.' But it's never quite that straightforward and this simple description belies a fair degree of complexity.

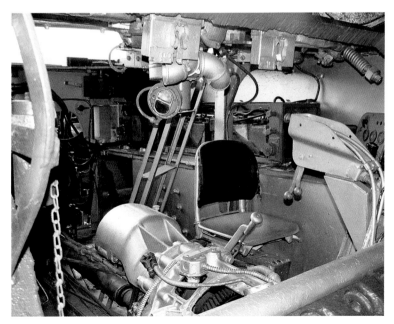

Engines

I n both Britain and the USA the production of sufficient quantities of tank engines constituted one of the most serious bottlenecks of the early years of the war; in the case of the USA, many engines originally intended for use in tanks were diverted to the US Navy. Eventually the shortages began to ease, but the situation regarding the supply of tank engines was never satisfactorily resolved, and the scarcity of suitable power units led to the adoption of engines that, in other circumstances, would hardly have been given a second look. Substitute engines – including the Chrysler A-57 multi-bank, the GM 6046D twin diesel and the Caterpillar D-200A – were adopted, even though this played havoc with the logistics of parts supply and field maintenance. As late as 1943 General John K. Christmas, who headed up the Ordnance Board's Tank and Combat Vehicle Division, had written in a letter to Major General Lucius Clay, ASF Director of Materiel, that it was the War Department's goal to use just one type of engine in the M4 tank... nevertheless, he went on to outline perfectly good reasons why it was necessary to continue with the existing multiplicity of types.

Five different engines were used during the

production life of the Sherman. The original power unit, and the most numerous, was the Wright (or Continental) nine-cylinder radial, but the most successful by a mile – and the power unit that was preferred by the US Army – was the Ford GAA, a V8 petrol engine of more than 18 litres.

All M4s were also fitted with a small auxiliary two-cylinder Homelite HRUH-28 two-stroke engine inside the hull. This was coupled to a 30V 50A generator designed to charge the batteries when the main engine was shut down, and to supplement the main generator during periods of high electrical demand.

Caterpillar D-200A

Dating from 1942, the Caterpillar D-200A (officially described as 'Ordnance engine RD-1820', the code indicating a radial diesel engine of 1,820in^3) was a supercharged four-stroke multi-fuel/diesel version of the Curtiss-Wright G-200 Cyclone 9, a nine-cylinder radial aircraft engine that had first seen the light of day in 1931.

The conversion work was carried out by the Caterpillar Tractor Company, specifically to produce a power unit suitable for medium and heavy tanks, and the engine was able to operate on a range of fuels including crude oil,

diesel oil, 100-octane petrol and even aviation spirit. The single-row radial configuration resulted in a power unit with rather more height and width than was ideal, and the excessive height necessitated the installation of a front-mounted transfer case to drop the line of drive from the crankshaft down to the tank's propeller shaft, whilst clearance 'blisters' were required in both the floor and the engine covers. To provide adequate cooling in the enclosed environment

ABOVE Sectional view of the GM Detroit Diesel-engined M4A2. *(Warehouse Collection)*

BELOW View of the two-cylinder Homelite HRUH-28 two-stroke auxiliary engine and generator. *(Warehouse Collection)*

**Ghost view of Ford-engined
M4A3 with 75mm gun.**

1 Track grouser
2 Spare track shoes
3 Rear stowage rack
4 Shovel; part of Pioneer
 tool kit, also includes axe
 and matchet
5 Jerrycans for fuel and
 water
6 Crew bedroll
7 Rear light
8 Recovery cable
9 Rear carburettor
10 Ford GAA V8 petrol
 engine
11 Engine air intake trunking
12 Fuel supply hose
13 Fuel filler guard
14 Radio antenna
15 Socket for machine gun
 mount
16 0.50in Browning M2
 heavy machine gun
17 Loader's hatch
18 Periscope
19 Commander's cupola
20 Breech of main gun
21 Hull extract ventilator
22 Loader's seat
23 Commander's seat
24 Turret lifting ring
25 Gunner's telescopic sight
26 Spare track shoes used
 to increase armoured
 protection in vulnerable
 areas of turret
27 Gun mantlet
28 Headlamp
29 75mm M3 main gun
30 Spare road wheel
31 Spare track shoes
32 0.30in Browning
 M1919A4 machine gun
33 Hull lifting ring
34 Final drive
35 Track drive sprocket
36 Spare ammunition for
 bow machine gun
37 Transmission

38 Co-driver's seat
39 Gunner's seat
40 Road wheel
41 VVSS suspension
 bracket
42 Volute suspension arm
43 Track shoe
44 Track return roller
45 Rear idler wheel

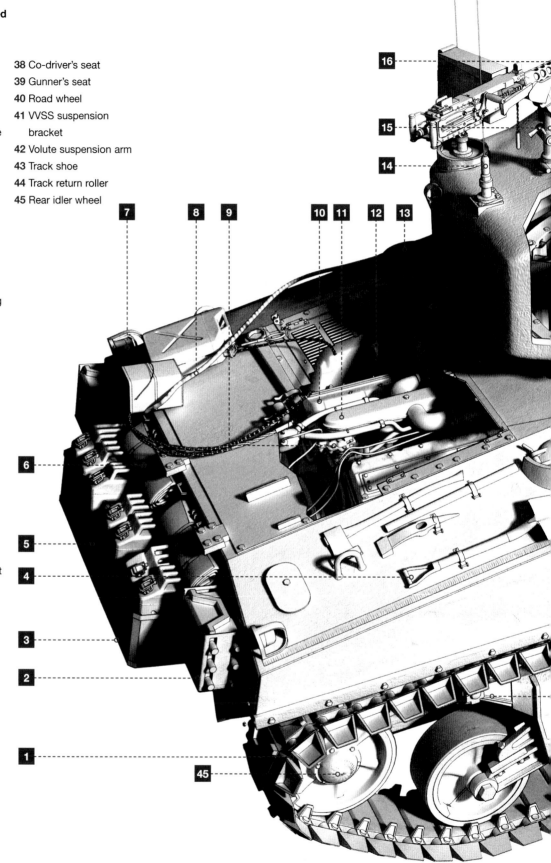

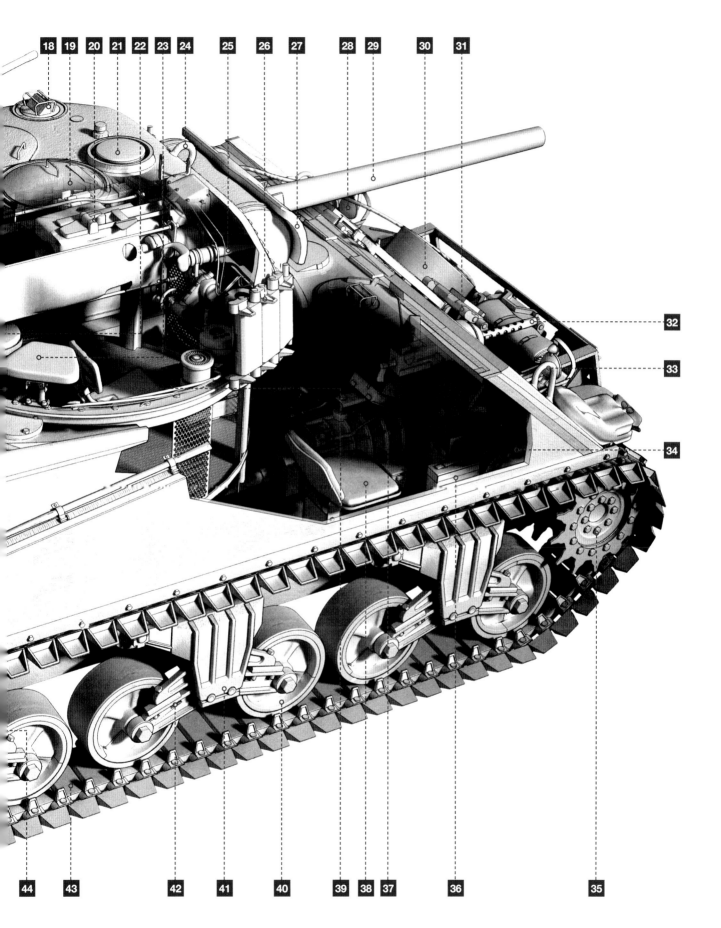

of the tank engine compartment, a large fan was attached to the flywheel at the rear to provide a flow of cooling air across the cylinders and through the oil cooler. The supercharger, the connecting rods and the cylinder barrels were taken from the Wright engine, whilst the pistons, cylinder heads, crankcase and injection equipment were designed by Caterpillar. Each cylinder head had two valves, operated by pushrods, with the exhaust valves being sodium-filled for cooling; there was also a separate injection pump for each of the nine cylinders. The supercharger was of the centrifugal type.

Rarest of all of the M4 Sherman engines, it is said that only 120 examples of the engine were constructed and it was fitted into just 75 M4A6 tanks before the Ordnance Board took the decision to concentrate production on the petrol-engined M4A3. Production was cancelled in February 1944 and none of these engines left the USA.

Chrysler A-57 multi-bank

Although undeniably ingenious, with five six-cylinder banks assembled around a common crankcase, each complete with its own crankshaft, camshaft, carburettor, manifolds, starter and distributor, Chrysler's A-57 multi-bank engine was, at the same time, a triumph of complexity over practicality. It had been

devised in something of a hurry by engineers at Chrysler's Detroit Tank Arsenal and was originally designed for use in the M3A4 medium tank, before also being adopted for the M4A4.

Design work started in late 1941, with the intention that the engine could be put into production as quickly as possible, and rather than starting with a clean sheet of paper Chrysler's design team used the maximum number of standard components. This, in turn, allowed the use of existing machines and tools. The side-valve blocks and the cylinder heads were derived from Chrysler's Royal engine, a 4.12-litre six-cylinder unit, with the heads redesigned to reduce the compression ratio from 6.8:1 to a more modest 6.2:1. The outputs from the five individual crankshafts were transferred to a ring gear and thence to a central shaft, and to the transmission. Constructed largely from cast iron, it was the heaviest of the engines used in the M4, and although between them the 30 cylinders had a capacity of 20,533cc, the maximum power output was just 425bhp, some 75bhp less than the far simpler and considerably lighter Ford GAA engine. In addition its overall size necessitated lengthening the hull to accommodate it.

Although there were considerable difficulties with the first prototype due to the differing lengths of the inlet tracts, the first experimental engine was installed in a tank on 15 November 1941. This tank was put through a 4,000-mile (6,500km) trial through the winter of 1941/42, and production got under way in the spring of 1942. Before the engine went into production, the carburettors – which were the standard Carter TD-1 of the original Royal engine – were moved so that they were all at the same level. The distributors were moved to the ends of the camshafts, and, at the same time, the chains which had been used to drive the camshafts in the donor engine were replaced by gears, and the five individual water pumps were replaced by a single shaft-driven pump which served the entire power unit. Lubrication was by means of a dry-sump system, and an oil cooler was fitted to maintain the correct oil temperature.

It was said that the A-57 could still drive the tank into which it was fitted with up to 12 of its 30 cylinders not functioning, but nevertheless,

BELOW **The Chrysler A-57 multi-bank engine of the M4A4 was effectively five separate six-cylinder units, with a combined capacity of 20,533cc, assembled around a common crankcase; the total 425bhp power output of the five individual crankshafts was transferred to a ring gear and thence to a central shaft and to the transmission.** *(Barmaglot)*

even the manufacturers warned the Ordnance Board that it might not be 'an ideal tank engine', and there was pressure to abandon the A-57 from as early as April 1942. However, the shortage of suitable tank engines meant that it was still fitted into a total of 7,687 M4A2 variants, most of which went to the British Army under the Lend-Lease arrangement. The British Army's Royal Electrical & Mechanical Engineers (REME) reported that the engine was 'very reliable', with an anticipated life of around 2,000 miles (3,200km), providing sodium-filled exhaust valves were fitted. A further 5,000 engines were constructed as spares.

Continental or Wright R-975 radial

The Ordnance Department had started using radial aircraft engines in tanks before the war, specifying the Continental R-670, which was later redesignated W-670. As tanks became heavier it was obvious that the 250bhp produced by the R-670 would not be adequate, and that a larger engine would be required. In 1938 the supercharged Wright R-975 Whirlwind was selected and it was successfully installed in the T5 medium tank.

Introduced in 1928, the R-975 formed part of a family of similar power units designed by the Wright Aeronautical Division of the Curtiss-Wright Corporation, originally for use in aircraft. The range included five-, seven- and nine-cylinder variants, each sharing common components, and at the time of its launch the R-975 was the most powerful in this line-up. It was designated J-6 Whirlwind Nine, or J-6-9, but following its adaptation for use in tanks Wright used the US Ordnance Board's R-975 designation.

The four-stroke air-cooled R-975 was a compact, lightweight and powerful overhead-valve engine, fitted with a gear-driven supercharger. For this application it was produced in two sub-variants: the R-975-C1, with a gross power output of 400bhp from a capacity of 15,928cc, and the improved R-975-C4, which put out 460bhp gross from the same capacity; both were fitted with twin spark plugs, with two valves per cylinder operated by pushrods. To compensate for the nature of the installation, a large multi-bladed

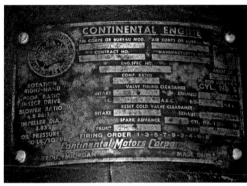

LEFT Data plate from a Continental R-975-C4 engine, giving basic performance and maintenance data. *(Warehouse Collection)*

ABOVE View down into the engine compartment showing the Wright (or Continental) R-975 nine-cylinder radial engine that was used in the M4, M4A1 and M4A5 variants; this power unit produced 400–460bhp from a capacity of 15,928cc. The radial configuration resulted in a tall but narrow engine, necessitating its being tilted towards the front of the tank to allow the propeller shaft to run under the floor. *(Ian Young)*

fan was attached directly to the crankshaft nose and surrounded by a sheet metal shroud to direct the air across the cylinders. The original 16in (400mm) Lipe twin-plate clutch tended to give trouble, and was eventually replaced by a larger Borg & Beck unit with a diameter of 17.5in (445mm).

A total of 18,284 M4, M4A1 and M4A5 tanks were equipped with this engine, making it the most numerous of the power units. However, it wasn't an ideal tank engine, having been designed to operate at a constant speed, and although reported as being 'reliable' it nevertheless suffered from a number of shortcomings, notably a propensity to exhibit hydrostatic lock, and to leak oil at an unacceptable rate; it also had a tendency to foul the spark plugs when called upon to idle or operate at low revolutions for long periods. US ordnance repair teams all carried large numbers

of spark plugs to support tanks operating in combat conditions, and REME reported that engine life was scarcely better than 1,000 miles (1,600km) before piston-ring wear caused chronic oiling-up.

A shortage of manufacturing capacity during the war years also saw the engine constructed under licence by the Continental Aircraft Engine Company, and the R-975 remained in production until 1945, by which time around 7,000 had been produced by Wright; the Continental version was produced after the war in an improved form as the R-9A, continuing until the mid-1950s, by which time some 53,000 examples had been constructed.

Ford GAA V8

Although it was designed from the outset as a tank engine, the Ford GAA was effectively two-thirds of the V12 aircraft engine that Ford had designed in 1940 as a rival to the Rolls-Royce Merlin. Designated, perhaps retrospectively, as the GAC, Ford's engine was rejected by the US Army Air Corps in favour of an existing Allison V12 engine, but when Ford was asked to come up with a design for a 500bhp power unit for the M4 medium tank it seemed expedient to

use elements of the rejected aircraft engine.

Work on the GAA started in September 1941, with the first model completed in January of the following year. The result was a superb piece of work – compact, powerful and reliable, with an excellent power-to-weight ratio, and there is little doubt that had there been sufficient production capacity the Ford GAA engine would have been fitted to all Shermans. To this day the Ford GAA remains a favourite with hot-rodders who are fortunate enough to lay their hands on one.

Designed around a one-piece cast-aluminium cylinder block with a 60° angle between the banks of cylinders, and press-fit dry liners, the engine featured double overhead cams, shaft-driven through a power-divider gearbox, with the cams acting directly on the valves, of which there were four per cylinder. All of the engine accessories were shaft-driven via this gearbox, housed at the front end of the block. The huge crankshaft was a flat 180° design, and any roughness in the engine was effectively damped out by the massive 225lb (102kg) combined weight of the flywheel and dual-disc clutch. Early engines used splayed four-bolt main bearings, although for later examples the design was simplified and just two bolts were used. Fuel was supplied at a prodigious rate through a pair of twin-barrel Stromberg carburettors, located at each end of the engine, and sparks were provided by a pair of four-cylinder magnetos, together with one four-cylinder distributor for each cylinder bank. The total power output was 500bhp gross (governed) from a capacity of 18,026cc, and huge amounts of torque were available right through the revs range.

A total of 28,000 GAA engines, including the related GAF and higher-powered GAN, were constructed, of which 12,596 were installed in the Sherman M4A3 variant; the engine was also manufactured in the original V12 configuration as the GAC, and this was used in the experimental T29 heavy tank.

GM 6046D twin diesels

The General Motors (GM) 6046D twin diesel was another expedient design intended to overcome the shortage of suitable power units, and had originally been specified for the M3A5

ABOVE Rated at 500bhp from a capacity of 18,026cc, the Ford GAA engine was a V8 design that used elements of an earlier aircraft engine. Powerful and reliable, the GAA was fitted into the M4A3 variant and was the engine favoured by the US Army. *(Ian Young)*

Lee/Grant tank, only later being adopted for the Sherman M4A2. In truth it was not one engine at all, but was actually a pair of GM 6-71 six-cylinder two-stroke diesels close-coupled side by side, with the output shafts meshed together via helical gears; a single output flange provided an attachment point for the propeller shaft that was connected to the tank's transmission. Although the arrangement was hardly ideal, the engines were at least dependable and easily maintained, and provided more power than the original Wright radials, even if synchronisation of the two power units sometimes presented something of a challenge... and the stalling of one engine led to an immediate halving of the amount of power available.

The 71 series – the figure '71' refers to the displacement in cubic inches – was introduced in 1938 by the Detroit Diesel Engine Division of General Motors, and was ultimately available in eight versions, with two-, three-, four- and six-cylinder in-line configurations, and as V8, V12 and V16 cylinder versions, all of them sharing as many components as possible. Parts of the range remain in production to this day. All 71 series engines are of similar design, with a gear-driven Roots-type supercharger providing intake air at slightly greater than atmospheric

pressure, delivered through cored passages in the engine block and ports in the cylinder walls. Burnt gases are exhausted through conventional poppet valves in the cylinder head, operated by pushrods. A single fuel injector and pump unit is provided for each cylinder, with the injection pump operating from the camshaft. For this application, although the engines were trialled with a dry-sump lubrication system, the decision was ultimately taken to adopt a conventional wet sump. The total displacement per engine was 6,965cc, and although the combined power output was 410bhp gross at 2,900rpm, there was a considerable weight penalty, with the installation weighing not much less than the Chrysler A-57 multi-bank unit.

A pilot vehicle was fitted with the 6046D at the end of December 1941, with testing continuing into the spring of the following year. The 6046D twin diesel power plant was fitted only into the M4A2, with a total of 10,968 tanks constructed. Many of these went to the Soviet Union and to Britain under the Lend-Lease arrangement, but because of the reduced risk of fire inherent in the use of diesel fuel, tanks fitted with the GM diesel engines were also favoured by the US Marine Corps for amphibious landings.

LEFT With a combined power output of 410bhp, the General Motors (GM) 6046D twin diesel of the M4A2 consisted of a pair of GM 6-71 six-cylinder two-stroke diesels close-coupled side by side; total displacement per engine was 6,965cc. *(Warehouse Collection)*

Table 6: Engine specifications

	Make and model					
	Caterpillar D-200A (RD-1820) radial	Chrysler A-57 multi-bank	Continental or Wright R-975-C1	Continental or Wright R-975-C4	Ford GAA V8	GM 6046D twin 6-71 diesels
Application	M4A6	M4A4	M4, M4A1	M4, M4A1, M4A5	M4A3	M4A2
Capacity	29,874cc; 1,823in³	20,533cc; 1,253in³	15,928cc; 972in³	15,928cc; 972in³	18,026cc; 1,100in³	13,929cc; 850in³
Cylinders	R9	30 (5 x in-line six)	R9	R9	V8, 60°	12 (2 x in-line six)
Bore x stroke	6.125 x 6.875in	4.37 x 4.5in	5 x 5.5in	5 x 5.5in	5.4 x 6in	4.25 x 5in
Compression ratio	15.5:1	6.2:1	5.7:1	5.7:1	7.5:1	16:1
Fuel	diesel, 40 cetane	petrol, 80 octane	petrol, 80 octane	petrol, 80 octane	petrol, 80 octane	diesel, 40 cetane
Induction system	supercharged	normally aspirated	supercharged	supercharged	normally aspirated	supercharged
Ignition	compression	battery	magneto	magneto	magneto	compression
Cooling system	air	liquid	air	air	liquid	liquid
Lubrication	dry sump	dry sump	dry sump	dry sump	wet sump	wet sump
Gross power output	497bhp at 3,000rpm	425bhp at 2,850rpm	400bhp at 2,400rpm	460bhp at 2,400rpm	500bhp at 2,600rpm	410bhp at 2,900rpm
Net power output	450bhp at 2,000rpm	370bhp at 2,400rpm	340bhp at 2,400rpm	400bhp at 2,400rpm	450bhp at 2,600rpm	375bhp at 2,100rpm
Gross torque	1,470lbf/ft at 1,200rpm	1,060lbf/ft at 1,400rpm	890lbf/ft at 1,800rpm	1,025lbf/ft at 1,800rpm	1,040lbf/ft at 2,200rpm	1,000lbf/ft at 1,400rpm
Net torque	945lbf/ft at 2,100rpm	1,020lbf/ft at 1,200rpm	800lbf/ft at 1,800rpm	940lbf/ft at 1,700rpm	950lbf/ft at 2,200rpm	885lbf/ft at 1,900rpm
Rotation (drive end)	anti-clockwise	anti-clockwise	anti-clockwise	anti-clockwise	anti-clockwise	anti-clockwise
Length	56in (1,422mm)	54.125in (1,375mm)	53in (1,346mm)	53in (1,346mm)	60.375in (1,534mm)	65.625in (1,667mm)
Width	55in (1,397mm)	58.75in (1,492mm)	45in (1,143mm)	45in (1,143mm)	33.25in (845mm)	59.375in (1,508mm)
Height	55in (1,397mm)	56.5in (1,435mm)	45in (1,143mm)	45in (1,143mm)	47.5in (1,207mm)	46.75in (1,187mm)
Dry weight	3,536lb (1,607kg)	5,400lb (2,455kg)	1,137lb (517kg)	1,137lb (517kg)	1,560lb (709kg)	5,110lb (2,323kg)

Fuel system

Fuel was drawn by a mechanical pump from four tanks, two vertical and two horizontal, located in the engine compartment; filters were placed between the tanks and the engine, and shut-off valves were provided to isolate the fuel supply whilst the tank was not running and to aid removal of the engine. Some variants were also fitted with an additional safety shut-off valve to prevent fuel leaking into the engine compartment.

The fuel capacity varied according to model: for the M4, M4A1 and M4A5 the capacity was 175 US gallons (146 gallons, 665 litres); the M4A2 has a maximum capacity of 148 US gallons (124 gallons, 560 litres); for the M4A3 the figure was 168 US gallons (140 gallons, 637 litres); for the M4A4 it was 160 US gallons (133 gallons, 606 litres); and for the M4A6 it was 138 US gallons (140 gallons, 637 litres).

RIGHT Twin fuel tanks are filled through flip-up caps on the engine decks: the fuel capacity varies according to the model, from 138 US gallons (140 imperial gallons, 637 litres) for the M4A6, to 175 US gallons (146 imperial gallons, 665 litres) for the M4, M4A1 and M4A5.
(Warehouse Collection)

Cooling system

The Wright, Continental and Caterpillar engines were air-cooled by means of a large fan fitted to the flywheel, arranged to draw air from outside the tank across the cooling fins of the cylinders.

The Chrysler, Ford and General Motors engines were liquid-cooled, with a sealed cooling system incorporating an expansion tank. For the purposes of description, the Ford engine is typical, with the liquid coolant circulated by a shaft-driven centrifugal pump, and with twin fans driven by twin belts and housed in sheet metal shrouds behind a large radiator at the very rear of the engine compartment. The bypass thermostat was designed to open at 140°F (60°C).

Transmission and final drive

Regardless of variant, the transmission and final-drive arrangements consisted of a clutch unit, a long propeller shaft running beneath the fighting compartment floor to convey the engine power to the gearbox, and a controlled differential incorporating the final-drive assemblies and the steering brakes. It is possible to remove the final-drive units separately, or to remove the complete transmission as a single assembly.

The clutch (or clutches) were supplied by either Borg & Beck or Lipe, and consisted of a double-disc dry unit, attached directly to the engine flywheel and operated via a pedal and a system of levers without any power assistance. On the GM 6046D-powered M4A2, each engine had its own clutch. A universally-jointed propeller beneath the floor of the fighting compartment coupled the engine to the

gearbox. The gearbox itself was a synchromesh unit offering five forward speeds and one reverse, with gear ratios of 7.56:1 (first gear), 3.11:1, 1.78:1, 1.11:1 and 0.73:1 (fifth gear); reverse gear was 5.65:1. There was no power assistance in the gearshift assembly and the gear-change lever was mounted directly to the gearbox top cover. An oil pump circulated lubricant around the gearbox and differential at pressure, and a cooling radiator was provided to maintain the oil at an appropriate temperature; a bypass valve, operating at 100°F (37.5°C), controlled the flow of oil through the cooler. The differential-drive bevel-gear ratio was 3.53:1, and the final-drive ratio 2.84:1, via a herringbone gear.

Initially transmissions were constructed by Caterpillar Tractor and the Iowa Transmission Company, the latter a subsidiary of the John Deere tractor company, but eventually the Detroit Arsenal was able to produce its own transmission units, and Buick, Ford and the Reed Roller Bit Company all made a contribution.

The track-drive sprockets were bolted to the final-drive shafts, and a lack of locating dowels on the drive sprockets sometimes led to breakages of the securing bolts. All of these units were assembled into the differential housing, which formed the forward portion of the hull, and which consisted either of a large one-piece casting, of which there were two patterns (one nicknamed 'Mary Ann' for its apparent likeness to the upper body area of a popular assembly-line worker at the Detroit Tank Arsenal), or of three parts bolted together, according to the specific variant. The one-piece nose simplified access to the differential and the final-drive system.

Steering brakes

There were two types of braking system used, both designed to operate directly on the differential output shafts. Described as single- and double-anchor brakes, each consisted of a three-shoe brake band, running in an oil bath. The brake bands were applied to the external face of the drums through a system of rods and levers, and, with no power assistance available, both the braking and steering systems called for considerable manual effort. The design of the differential did not allow a neutral turn (one track travelling forwards, the other in reverse) to be made, and even a

skid turn, with the tank pivoting around one stationary track, was difficult due to the sheer physical effort involved in stopping one track from rotating.

Both brakes could be pulled on and latched to provide a parking brake.

Suspension

On each side of the tank the tracks were supported on three bogies, each consisting of a huge cast-steel bracket on which was pivoted a pair of rubber-tyred road wheels, carried on leading and trailing arms; there were four different patterns of road wheel. Each of the bogie suspension units incorporated a pair of compact helically-wound volute springs that supported the weight of the tank. Steel skid

BELOW The vertical volute spring suspension system went through four design stages. Early units were like those used on the M3 medium tank, and had the return roller positioned on the top of the suspension casting; this was followed by a second pattern with a semi-circular spring-steel skid on the housing, but with the return roller carried on a bracket behind a more substantial housing. On the two subsequent designs the shape of the spring-steel skid was altered. The photograph shows the final design. *(Warehouse Collection)*

RIGHT The tracks were driven via a pair of 13-tooth flame-cut sprockets at the front, with at least two different designs fitted during the life of the tank; this is the early open-pattern sprocket. Some of the Canadian M4A5 variants used a special 17-tooth drive sprocket to suit the shorter-pitch Canadian dry-pin track. *(Warehouse Collection)*

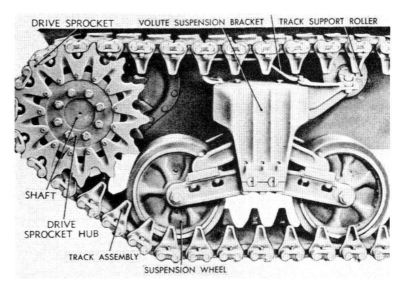

SHAFT

DRIVE
SPROCKET HUB

TRACK ASSEMBLY

SUSPENSION WHEEL

RIGHT Explanatory photograph showing the key elements of the drive and vertical volute spring suspension system. There were several designs of road wheel. *(Warehouse Collection)*

units and support rollers, attached to the tops of the suspension units, carried the upper track run. Changes were made during production to the diameter of the springs and to the track return rollers, with the rollers ultimately being carried on separate brackets, rather than centred on the suspension units.

The springs of the early M4s were positioned vertically, whence they were unsurprisingly known as 'vertical volute spring suspension' (VVSS) units. In March 1944 the US Ordnance Committee approved the use of a new, more durable 'horizontal volute spring suspension' (HVSS) system, which provided a more controlled ride and at the same time reduced the possibility of throwing tracks. The suspension was completely redesigned, placing the two springs alongside one another, in a horizontal position, between pivoting arms. Hydraulic damper units were fitted between the arms, above the springs, and the steel skid units on the upper track run were eliminated, with two additional return rollers fitted to brackets attached to the hull on either side. At the same time the width of the track was increased, which necessitated the use of paired road wheels to support the track. This was a huge improvement on the original system.

During the production and service life of the tank, there were various experiments with different suspension systems. For example, during early 1942 Chrysler was asked to look into the possibility of adapting the Christie coil-spring suspension system for use on the Sherman, but in the event nothing came of this project. In August 1943 an M4A4 was fitted with the suspension developed by Allis Chalmers for the T22 heavy tractor, but this

LEFT The horizontal volute spring suspension used pairs of springs and also incorporated shock absorbers to improve the ride, thus providing a more stable gun platform. It also allowed the use of wider tracks and reduced the tendency for the Sherman to throw tracks when turning.
(Warehouse Collection)

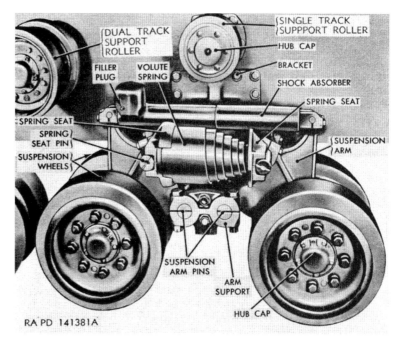

DUAL TRACK SUPPORT ROLLER

SINGLE TRACK SUPPPORT ROLLER

HUB CAP

BRACKET

SHOCK ABSORBER

FILLER PLUG

VOLUTE SPRING

SPRING SEAT

SPRING SEAT

SPRING SEAT PIN

SUSPENSION ARM

SUSPENSION WHEELS

SUSPENSION ARM PINS

ARM SUPPORT

HUB CAP

RA PD 141381A

RIGHT Explanatory photograph showing the key elements of the HVSS suspension system and track return rollers. Tanks fitted with HVSS suspension were generally designated 'E8', *eg* 'M4A3E8'. *(Warehouse Collection)*

proved to be susceptible to breakages and this project, too, was abandoned. The experimental Centipede used a variation of the leaf-spring suspension designed for the M3/M5 family of half-tracked vehicles, and there were also experiments with torsion-bar suspension (in the style of the M26 Pershing tank), in combination with volute rebound springs.

Tracks

The tracks consisted of a series of separate shoes linked together by steel pins inserted through the track link end connectors; both dry pins and rubber-bushed pins were employed, and the end connectors were designed to engage with the drive sprockets. The track pitch was 6in (150mm), with 79 shoes on all but the extended length M4A4, the latter having 83 shoes; some of the Canadian M4A5 Grizzlys used a shorter-pitch track (4.6in, 117mm) that required a special 17-tooth drive sprocket.

The tracks used on VVSS suspension were 16.56in (421mm) wide, whilst those used with the later HVSS suspension had an overall width of 23in (584mm). M4E2 variants were fitted with a 24in (610mm) wide cast-steel track, which necessitated spacing the bogie units away from the hull sides. Initially the tracks used rubber pads as a wearing surface, carried in pockets in the steel track sections, but one set of tank tracks required 1,734lb (788kg) of rubber, and following the invasion of South-East Asia by the Japanese in 1941 shortages of rubber led to the development of an all-steel track design, which started to be fitted from 1942.

During the production life of the vehicle several different patterns of track shoe were used, both with and without rubber pads, as follows:

Narrow track sections

T41	Double-pin reversible plain rubber block track.
T47	Double-pin cast-steel three-cleat track.
T47E1	Double-pin cast-steel three-cleat track.
T48	Double-pin rubber chevron-pattern track.
T49	Double-pin cast-steel parallel-bar track.
T51	Double-pin non-reversible plain rubber block track.
T54E1	Double-pin cast-steel chevron-pattern track.
T54E2	Double-pin cast-steel Chrysler 'cuff' chevron-pattern track.
T56	Double-pin cast-steel three-cleat track.
T56E1	Double-pin cast-steel chevron-pattern track.
T62	Double-pin cast-steel chevron-pattern track.
T74	Double-pin cast-steel chevron-pattern track.

Track sections used on M4A5 Grizzly tanks only

CDP   Canadian dry-pin track, 4.6in (117mm) pitch.

WE210   Non-reversible rubber track with double 'I' pattern.

Wide track sections

T65   Double-pin cast-steel track.

T66   Single-pin centre-guided cast-steel track.

T80   Double-pin cast-steel rubber-faced chevron track.

T80E5   Double-pin cast-steel rubber-faced chevron track (post-war Israeli design).

T84   Double-pin cast-steel rubber-faced chevron track.

Whilst the width of the tracks was generally narrower than those used on German tanks, resulting in a lack of manoeuvrability and a tendency for the Sherman to become easily bogged down in mud, the design of the tracks, combined with the use of rubber pads and rubber-tyred road wheels, gave the Sherman a better performance on the road, with a higher top speed and a more comfortable ride. In addition, a set of Sherman tracks could last as long as 2,500 miles (4,000km), whilst the life of the steel tracks of German tanks could be less than 500 miles (800km) under certain conditions.

Grousers

The standard ground pressure of the narrow-tracked Sherman was somewhere in the order of 13–15lbf/in^2 (0.91–1.1kg/cm^2), a high figure which meant that the tanks were easily bogged down in soft or wet soil. The pressure could be reduced by fitting end connectors with an extended length, and duckbill-shaped connectors – known as 'grousers' – were developed, which extended the track width to 20.125in (511mm) and increased the area of track in contact with the ground by some 20%.

Unfortunately it was not possible to fit the grouser to both sides of the track until 1944, when Chrysler devised a method of spacing the suspension away from the hull by 4.5in (114mm). With grousers fitted to both sides of the track, the effective track width was increased to 23.69in (602mm) and the ground

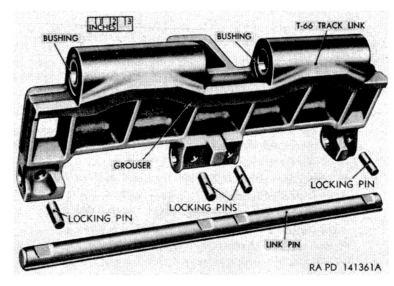

RA PD 141361A

pressure reduced to 10lbf/in^2 (0.73kg/cm^2). The use of spaced suspension is indicated by the suffix 'E9', *eg* M4A3E9.

Hull and turret

Face-hardened nickel-steel alloy armour plate had been first developed during the late 19th century to replace the considerable thickness of iron armour previously used in the construction of 'capital' warships. The early Harvey carburisation process – which entailed maintaining contact between the heated steel and carbon in the form of charcoal, often for weeks at a time – was quickly replaced by the German Krupp process. Krupp's steel armour included chromium in the mix, but, most importantly, carbon-bearing gases were applied directly to the heated steel. The carburised face was then rapidly heated to 30–40% of the steel's depth, before quickly quenching first the superheated side, then both sides of the steel, with jets of water or oil.

Then in 1882 a British metallurgist, Robert Hadfield, discovered that homogenous armour could be produced by the addition of manganese to the steel alloy, patenting his work in 1883/84 and publishing his findings in 1888. Hadfield's austenitic manganese steel – often described as mangalloy or 'Hadfield steel' – combined high toughness and ductility with high work-hardening capacity and good resistance to wear. During World War One Hadfield's manganese steel was used to produce armour plate, shells, tank treads and soldier's helmets.

ABOVE Disassembled view of the track shoe and link-pin system; some 20 different styles of track were used or trialled on the Sherman.
(Warehouse Collection)

Elsewhere the development of armoured steels continued, and in Germany it was found that producing rolled steel plates which alloyed 3 to 4% of nickel with 1.5 to 2% of chromium and small amounts (0.3 to 0.5%) of carbon, provided a material that was generally harder than standard carbon steel. In some cases the performance could be further improved by the addition of one of the rarer metals, such as tungsten or vanadium.

In the USA there had been little progress in the manufacture of armour, and in the interwar years American tanks were protected by relatively thin steel plates having a high nickel content, and hardened on the outer face. Because of the difficulties inherent in welding this material, American (and British) tanks of the period were of riveted construction. Following British experiences against German tanks in France in 1940 it became obvious that tanks would be required to withstand heavy calibre weapons, including artillery, and the maximum thickness of armour was quickly increased from 25mm to 75mm, and then 90mm – by 1945 the US Ordnance Board was considering the production of tanks with up to 250mm of armour. The face-hardened plates gave way to a material described as rolled homogeneous armour (RHA) that could be welded without

cracking or distortion, both to speed production and to improve the standard of protection.

The process of hot-rolling elongates and homogenises the grain structure of the steel, removing imperfections which might otherwise reduce its strength, and providing a uniform structure and composition throughout the thickness. The resulting material allows stresses – caused, for example, by the impact of an armour-piercing projectile – to flow through the metal, rather than being concentrated in one area. Most tank armour produced during World War Two was of the RHA type, and the US Ferrous Metallurgical Advisory Board helped to develop new techniques for casting, heat treating and welding tank steel; for example, in the latter case adding molybdenum to the alloy was found to ease the problems of welding.

At the same time, the angular-shaped hulls and turrets forced on the designers by the necessity of riveting flat plates together began to be superseded by cast components with rounded contours. Attention was also being paid to the importance of the geometry of the glacis plate, with some consensus emerging that a ricochet could be generated from an angle of 38° from the horizontal.

Although the hulls of the M4 and the earlier M3 were produced as huge one-piece castings, a

lack of production capacity for such large castings meant that welding remained the favoured approach for constructing hulls. Nevertheless, the production of both rolled and cast homogeneous armour – the latter abbreviated to CHA – was increased enormously as the war progressed, and by late 1942, with the assistance of finance from the Defense Plant Corporation, something like 57,000 tons of cast armour was being produced every month. The Ford Motor Company built a new foundry capable of producing 1,000 tons of armour per month, half of which was cast, and American Car & Foundry expanded production to become the largest producer of face-hardened armour plate in the USA.

Hull design

Most Sherman variants were of welded construction, with only the M4A1 and M4A5 using a cast hull, and the so-called M4 composite (or hybrid) having a cast nose and glacis plate welded to a fabricated rear section, with the cast section extending from the differential housing to the forward edge of the turret ring. Regardless of the form of construction, the hull was divided into three areas, consisting of the driving compartment at the front, the fighting compartment in the centre, and the engine at the rear. The turret

ABOVE LEFT Steel hull and turret castings were supplied by almost 40 different manufacturers, including American Steel Foundries, Columbia Steel Company, Continental Foundry and Machine Company, General Steel Castings Corporation, Pittsburgh Steel Foundry Corporation, and Union Steel Castings. The 'G' mark on this casting indicates that it came from the Granite City works of American Steel Foundries in Illinois. *(Warehouse Collection)*

ABOVE Photographed during disembarkation training in 1943, these Shermans have the distinctive cast upper hull of the M4A1 (and M4A5). The first ever one-piece cast upper tank hull was produced by General Steel Castings Corporation in 1939. *(Warehouse Collection)*

LEFT The distinctive three-piece bolted differential housing was used on all M4A4 variants and on other early production machines before the one-piece cast nose was adopted. *(Warehouse Collection)*

was placed in the centre of the hull and was bolted to the turret ring so that it remained free to rotate on a ball race. Entry to and exit from the vehicle was by means of crew access hatches, and there was an emergency escape hatch in the floor. Drain valves were fitted to the bottom of the hull to allow accumulated water or fuel to be removed.

Although necessarily cramped, the hull provided accommodation for a crew of up to five men, albeit losses amongst tank crews during the Battle of the Bulge sometimes saw the number of crew reduced to three. The driver and co-driver/bow gunner were placed at the front, with the driver seated alongside the transmission, and the co-driver on top of it; the men also shared this space with the differential and final-drive components, which were bolted across the entire width of the front part of the hull. The commander, gunner and loader were accommodated in the fighting compartment. A fireproof bulkhead separated the engine compartment from the fighting compartment, and doors at the rear allowed access to the engine for routine maintenance; hinged and removable covers over the engine compartment allowed the engine to be extracted for repair or replacement. The propeller shaft conveying power from the engine at the rear to the transmission at the front ran under the floor of the fighting compartment, and the suspension and track-return components were attached directly to the lower hull.

Constant changes were made to the

specification, but the hull generally also included either periscopes or direct-vision slots for the driver, a periscope for the co-driver/bow gunner, and one or more exhaust fans.

Field-applied *appliqué* armour

Unhappy with the thickness of armour provided by the factory, many US Army Sherman crews took matters into their own hands and came up with various ingenious ways of increasing the thickness of the frontal areas of the tank. Photographs show that steel plates and spare track shoes were often welded to the glacis plate, and sometimes to the turret sides and the hull, in the hope of perhaps deflecting a stray shot or of absorbing some of the kinetic energy before it reached the surface of the armour. Sandbags – sometimes filled with concrete and sometimes bedded in concrete – heavy baulks of timber and bogie wheels were also carried on the glacis plate, and occasionally on the flanks of the vehicle in carefully constructed racks. Some crews applied layers of concrete, sometimes to a thickness of three or four inches (75–100mm) and often reinforced with chicken wire, to produce a kind of makeshift 'armoured' paste, which placed additional strain on the forward suspension bogies. It is doubtful that any of these techniques – none of which was officially approved – were particularly successful against armour-piercing rounds, but presumably the additional thickness gave the crew some additional sense of security. The practice was far less prevalent amongst British Army Shermans, but this may simply have indicated a different discipline regime.

An official modification saw *appliqué* armoured steel plates measuring approximately 18 x 24in (457 x 610mm) in size, and 1in (25.4mm) in thickness, welded to the sides of the hull over the ammunition storage racks in an effort to prevent penetration in these areas. At the same time the racks themselves were enclosed in 0.25in (6mm) thick armoured-steel boxes, with hinged armoured doors. Patches were welded to the glacis plate immediately in front of the driver's and co-driver's positions. Additional armour was also welded to the right-hand front face of the turret, where the armour had been reduced in thickness to accommodate the powered traverse gear.

ABOVE In an attempt to prevent penetration of the hull in the area of the ammunition storage racks, which often resulted in the tank brewing-up, *appliqué* armoured steel plates – approximately 18 x 24in (457 x 610mm) in size, and 1in (25.4mm) thick – were welded to the sides of the hull. The racks themselves were enclosed in 0.25in (6mm) thick armoured-steel boxes, with hinged armoured doors. *(Warehouse Collection)*

Turret design

Regardless of the hull and automotive arrangements, and disregarding minor modifications, all of the Shermans equipped with the 75mm gun or the 105mm howitzer shared what was essentially the same basic turret design. It had a gently rounded profile and a flat top, with a sloping front; a weight was attached at the rear to counterbalance the gun and there was a rotating turret basket in which the seats for the commander, gunner and loader were mounted. The turret roof included a rotating commander's cupola, and from December 1943 on there was also a separate access hatch for the loader. In Britain, Dr Pochin of the Medical Research Council devised an all-round vision cupola that was fitted with eight periscopes. The cupola was fitted to the Sherman turret by means of a special ring and was interchangeable with similar cupolas fitted to the Churchill and Cromwell tanks. Although a final design was produced by the Department of Tank Design, it does not appear that this cupola was adopted. A powered ventilator was fitted into the roof to remove fumes that could build up whilst the gun was being fired. Early M4s

ABOVE Late model M4A3 fitted with experimental Flintkote HCR2 plastic armour on the sides of the hull and turret. This armour, which was attached in panel form, consisted of 10in (254mm) deep aluminium-faced panels containing a mixture of gravel, mastic asphalt and wood flour. Tests carried out at Aberdeen Proving Ground in late 1945 showed that the HCR2 armour could defeat the German *Panzerfaust* 100 or an 88mm shell. *(Tank Museum)*

BELOW All of the 75mm- and 105mm-gun Shermans shared what was essentially the same basic turret design, with a sloping front, a gently rounded profile and a flat top. A weight at the rear was used to counterbalance the gun. *(Warehouse Collection)*

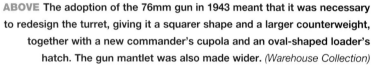

ABOVE The adoption of the 76mm gun in 1943 meant that it was necessary to redesign the turret, giving it a squarer shape and a larger counterweight, together with a new commander's cupola and an oval-shaped loader's hatch. The gun mantlet was also made wider. *(Warehouse Collection)*

ABOVE Most of the turrets for the 75mm gun and all of the new turrets for the 76mm gun were fitted with a hinged pistol port on the left-hand side. *(Warehouse Collection)*

were also provided with a pistol port in the left-hand side wall of the hull; these were deleted in February 1943, only to be reintroduced the following year.

The turret was carried on a 69in (1,753mm) diameter ball race that allowed it to be traversed through a full 360°, and both manual and powered turret-traversing systems were fitted. Powered traverse systems were supplied by the Oilgear Company, Logansport and Westinghouse, the first two systems being hydraulic, the third electric. The hydraulic traverse systems gave a smoother action and were easier to maintain.

RIGHT Annotated view of the commander's cupola in the turret roof. *(Warehouse Collection)*

FAR RIGHT Dr Pochin of the Medical Research Council devised an all-round vision cupola with eight periscopes that could be fitted to the Sherman turret by means of a special ring. The cupola is shown in both the opened and closed positions. *(Warehouse Collection)*

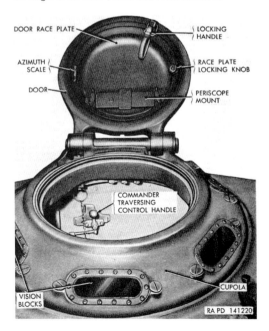

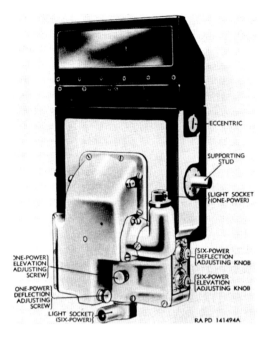

ECCENTRIC

SUPPORTING STUD

(LIGHT SOCKET (ONE-POWER)

(ONE-POWER) ELEVATION ADJUSTING SCREW)

(SIX-POWER DEFLECTION ADJUSTING KNOB)

(SIX-POWER ELEVATION ADJUSTING KNOB)

ONE-POWER DEFLECTION ADJUSTING SCREW)

LIGHT SOCKET (SIX-POWER)

RA PD 141494A

ABOVE Early production vehicles were fitted with a single M6 driver's periscope, as seen here, giving forward vision only. In 1944 this was replaced by the M13 prism, which was a solid block of plastic with a prism shape and a reflective surface moulded into each end. Later machines had a second periscope that could be rotated through 360° and tilted to raise or lower the line of vision, and other crew members (except the gunner) were also provided with an M6 or M13 periscope. *(Warehouse Collection)*

When the 76mm gun was adopted in 1943 it was fitted into a new turret with a redesigned commander's cupola and an oval-shaped loader's hatch. The new turret is easily recognised by its squarer shape, larger counterweight at the rear and wider gun mantlet, and the combination of the new shape and the larger gun gave the tank an altogether more business-like appearance – which, unfortunately, was not reflected in its performance, which was scarcely any better. At the same time the turret basket was modified, later to be eliminated altogether, which necessitated attaching the commander's and loader's seats to the turret rim.

The turret on the M4A3E2 assault tank resembled that used on the 76mm gun tanks, but was a different casting of a considerably thicker and heavier design in all areas except the roof.

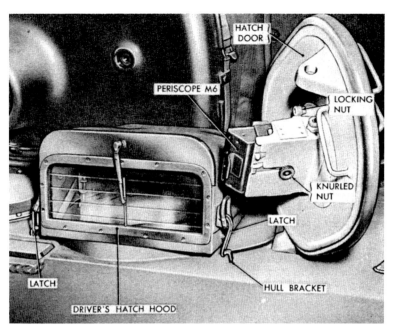

HATCH DOOR

PERISCOPE M6

LOCKING NUT

KNURLED NUT

LATCH

LATCH

HULL BRACKET

DRIVER'S HATCH HOOD

ABOVE Annotated view of the removable weather hood and windscreen wiper for the driver's hatch. *(Warehouse Collection)*

Interior lighting

Three dome lights were mounted in the ceiling of the turret, and two in the ceiling of the driving compartment. Each light was controlled by a separate toggle switch and was equipped with two lamps, the lenses of which were divided into red and white sections. A safety latch prevented the white light being turned on accidentally.

There was also an extension light mounted on the turret ceiling, with 10ft (3,050mm) of cable in a self-winding retractable coil.

Finish

The tanks left the factory with an overall external coating of matt olive green paint. Although the colour was supposedly standardised as Olive Drab there were two separate references, with the Quartermaster Corps describing the colour as 'number 22' and the Corps of Engineers referring to it as 'colour 9'; other colour references can also be found in period material, including 'ES-474' and 'ES-680'. In January 1943 the colour was eventually standardised as 'A/N 319' Olive Drab, and in August 1945 the finish was changed to semi-

Table 7: Armour thickness

Note that the effective thickness of the armour increases by virtue of being sloped on various parts of the hull.

Variant:												
M4		M4A1		M4A2		M4A3			M4A3E2	M4A4	M4A5	M4A6
75mm	*105mm*	*75mm*	*76mm*	*75mm*	*76mm*	*75mm*	*76mm*	*105mm*	*75mm*	*75mm*	*75mm*	*75mm*
Hull												
Front upper												
51mm	64mm	51mm	64mm	64mm	64mm	51mm*	64mm	64mm	102mm	51mm	51mm	51mm
(angle from vertical) 56°	47°	37–55°	37–55°	47°	47°	56°	47°	47°	47°	56°	37–55°	51°
Front lower 51mm	51–108mm	51mm	51–108mm	51–108mm	51–108mm	51mm*	51–108mm	51–108mm	114–140mm	51mm	51mm	51–108mm
(angle from vertical) 0–56°	0–56°	0–45°	0–56°	0–56°	0–56°	0–56°	0–56°	0–56°	0–56°	0–45°	0–45°	0–56°
Sides 38mm	38mm	38mm	38mm	38mm	38mm	38mm	38mm	38mm	38–76mm	38mm	38mm	38mm
Rear 38mm	38mm	38mm	38mm	38mm	38mm	38mm	38mm	38mm	38mm	38mm	38mm	38mm
Top 19mm	19mm	13–19mm	19mm	19mm	19mm	19mm	19mm	19mm	19mm	19mm	13-19mm	19mm
Floor, front 25mm	25mm	25mm	25mm	25mm	25mm	25mm	25mm	25mm	25mm	25mm	25mm	25mm
Floor, rear 13mm	13mm	13mm	13mm	13mm	13mm	13mm	13mm	13mm	13mm	13mm	13mm	13mm
Method of construction weldedâ€	weldedâ€	cast	cast	welded	welded	welded	welded	welded	welded	welded	cast	welded
Turret												
Gun shield 89mm	91mm	76mm	89mm	89mm	89mm	89mm	89mm	89mm	178mm	76mm	76mm	89mm
Gun rotor shield 51mm	–	51mm	–	51mm	–	51mm	–	–	–	51mm	51mm	51mm
Front 76mm	76mm	76mm	64mm	76mm	64mm	76mm	64mm	76mm	152mm	76mm	76mm	76mm
Sides 51mm	51mm	76mm	64mm	51mm	64mm	51mm	64mm	51mm	152mm	51mm	76mm	51mm
Rear 51mm	51mm	51mm	64mm	51mm	64mm	51mm	64mm	51mm	152mm	51mm	51mm	51mm
Roof 25mm	25mm	25mm	25mm	25mm	25mm	25mm	25mm	25mm	25mm	25mm	25mm	25mm

* Figures increased to 64mm (front upper) and 51–108mm (front lower) for tanks with wet ammunition storage.

† M4 composite used a hybrid rolled and cast construction.

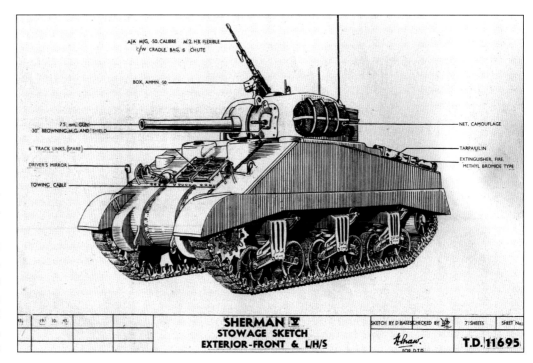

RIGHT British Army stowage diagram for the M4A4 (Sherman V) showing the main and secondary weapons and the items approved for carrying on the external surfaces of the hull.
(Tank Museum)

gloss, when the reference number became '202'. By 1949 it was being referred to as '2430'. In the field various finishes were applied over the factory paint, either as a single overall colour or in a two-colour disruptive pattern to suit the local terrain and weather conditions: for example, sand; sand and tan; green and maroon; white; white and green, etc.

The internal finish for the hull, engine compartment and turret was gloss white. The paint exhibited a slight yellowish tinge due to the use of natural resins and lead pigments in its manufacture.

Standard external markings included the USA registration number stencilled in blue, and later in white, on the nose and at the rear of the hull, and the US national star painted in matt white at the front of the hull and on the sides of the hull and turret. Unit markings were generally also applied to the front and rear of the hull.

Tanks serving with the British, Canadian, Soviet and Free French were similarly finished and marked, but the Canadian and Free French vehicles also carried their own national recognition symbols.

Main gun

75mm M2 and M3 tank gun

The original short-barrelled M2 75mm weapon fitted to the Sherman was a rifled light artillery gun with a total length from breech to muzzle of 91.75in (2,330mm), giving a length-to-calibre ratio of L/32. A large counterweight was clamped around the muzzle. Muzzle velocity when firing armour-piercing capped, ballistic capped (APCBC) ammunition was 1,930ft/sec (590m/s), which allowed the gun to penetrate 55mm of armour at a range of 1,000 yards (915m). Loading was effected manually, and the breech was opened automatically by the recoil of the gun and closed automatically under spring pressure as a new round was loaded.

The M2 75mm gun was quickly replaced by the longer-barrelled M3, without a counterweight and with a length from breech to muzzle of 118.38in (3,007mm), giving a length-to-calibre ratio of L/40.1. The muzzle velocity with armour-piercing capped (APC) rounds was 2,030ft/sec (619m/s), allowing

the projectile to penetrate 59mm of armour at 1,000 yards (915m). Maximum rate of fire was 20 rounds a minute. The 75mm gun was originally carried in the M34 gun mount, bolted to the front face of the turret and designed to support both the main gun and a co-axial machine gun, and allowing manual elevation and depression of the two guns via a hand wheel through a range of +25° to −12°. A cast rotor shield protected the gun-barrel bearing surface and prevented shrapnel and other flying debris from entering the turret; a separate shield protected the co-axial machine gun. The mount did not include a direct-vision telescopic sight, but the gunner was provided with an overhead periscope projecting through the turret roof in front of the commander's cupola, which offered an indirect view. In October 1942 the original mount was replaced by the improved M34A1, which had a larger external rotor shield and a small opening for a direct-view telescopic sight. The maximum elevation was unchanged at +25°, but the maximum depression was reduced to −10°. The increased weight of the new mount necessitated the addition of a counterweight, but this time on the breech of the main gun.

Both 75mm guns were authorised to fire a range of standard ammunition types, including armour-piercing solid shot (AP); armour-piercing

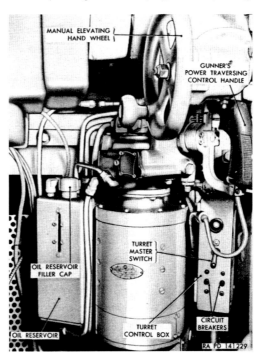

LEFT Annotated view of the turret controls for the early 75mm M2 gun. *(Warehouse Collection)*

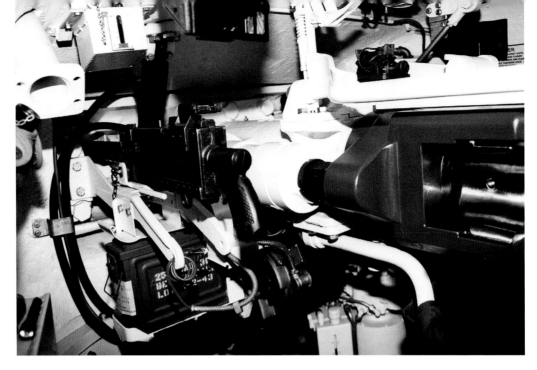

RIGHT Restored
vehicle showing the
breech of the 76mm
M1 main gun and the
turret machine gun.
(Ian Young)

solid shot with tracer (AP-T); armour-piercing
capped (APC); armour-piercing capped with
tracer (APC-T); armour-piercing capped, ballistic
capped (APCBC); hyper-velocity armour-
piercing (HVAP); hyper-velocity armour-piercing
with tracer (HVAP-T); hyper-velocity target
practice with tracer (HVTP-T); high explosive,
either with impact, 'superquick' or variable delay
fuse (HE); high explosive with tracer (HEP-T);
and white phosphorus smoke (WP) rounds.
There were also blank and drill practice rounds.
See Table 8, page 92.

76mm M1 tank gun

By late 1942 it was obvious that the original
75mm M3 gun was insufficiently powerful and
it was suggested that it might be replaced

by the 3in M7 gun that was carried in the
M10 tank destroyer. In the event there was
insufficient space in the Sherman turret and
this necessitated the development of a new
gun that could fire the same projectiles as the
3in M7, but using a longer projectile case that
provided greater muzzle velocity. The sliding,
semi-automatic breech was similar to that used
on the 75mm gun, and the maximum rate of
fire was also 20 rounds a minute. Although
the new gun was also of 3in calibre, it was
designated as the 76mm M1 tank gun in order
to differentiate it from the M7 weapon. The gun
was carried in the M62 mount, which provided
a maximum elevation of +25° and a maximum
depression of −10°. The mount also included
provision for a co-axial machine gun.

Production of the M1 L/57 variant started in
late 1943, but this was soon replaced by the
M1A1, in which the barrel length was reduced
to L/52 in an attempt to correct the balance,
and a small counterweight was mounted on the
muzzle. The later M1A2 also had the pitch of the
rifling reduced, and included provision for the
addition of a muzzle brake to deflect the blast
of the gun to the sides and to the rear, thus
reducing the recoil forces, and minimising the
space required inside the turret to accommodate
the recoil itself. This also had the advantage of
reducing wear on the recoil mechanism. Most
of the M1A1 guns were subsequently converted
to accept the muzzle brake, in which form they
were described as M1A1C.

Authorised standard ammunition types

BELOW Annotated
view of the breech of
the 75mm M3 main
gun and the M34
or M34A1 mount.
(Warehouse Collection)

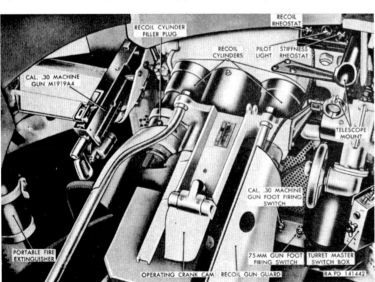

included armour-piercing solid shot (AP); armour-piercing solid shot with tracer (AP-T); armour-piercing capped (APC); armour-piercing capped with tracer (APC-T); hyper-velocity armour-piercing (HVAP); hyper-velocity armour-piercing with tracer (HVAP-T); hyper-velocity target practice with tracer (HVTP-T); high explosive, either with impact, 'superquick' or variable delay fuse (HE); high explosive with tracer (HEP-T); and white phosphorus smoke (WP) rounds. There were also blank and drill practice rounds. See Table 8, page 92.

17-pounder Mk IV and Mk VII tank gun

Dating from 1943, the British Ordnance quick-firing (QF) 17-pounder (76.2mm) gun, in Mk IV or Mk VII configuration, was the most powerful gun fitted into the Sherman during the war, and was also the best Allied anti-tank gun of the period. The size of the gun meant that it had to be rolled through 90°, effectively laying it on its side, to allow it to fit into the Sherman turret, and a large box was required at the back of the turret to accommodate the considerable recoil. The British-designed mount, described as 'mounting, number 2, Mk 1', provided a maximum elevation of +20°, and a maximum depression of −5°.

Suitable ammunition types included armour-piercing capped, ballistic capped (APCBC), the then-innovatory armour-piercing discarding sabot (APDS), and impact-fused high explosive (HE) rounds, and the maximum rate of fire was ten rounds a minute; see Table 11, page 114. When firing APDS rounds the muzzle velocity was 3,950ft/sec (1,205m/s), meaning that the gun was capable of penetrating up to 170mm of armour at a range of 1,000 yards (915m).

Shermans that were fitted with the 17-pounder (76.2mm) gun were described as Fireflys, and eventually 50% of Shermans in British service were converted to this configuration. Some official literature also uses the name Mayfly.

105mm M2A1 and M4 howitzer

Although production did not start until 1944, trials of the 105mm M4 howitzer had started in November 1942 with a view to providing artillery support for armoured formations. The gun itself

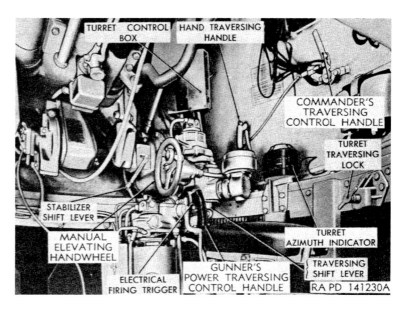

was a modification of the towed M2A1 howitzer and, like the British QF 17-pounder, it was necessary to turn the gun on to its side in order to fit it into the turret, meaning that the breech was loaded from the side rather than the top. The maximum rate of fire was just eight rounds a minute. The 105mm howitzer was carried in the T70 or M52 mount, providing a maximum elevation of +35° and a maximum depression of −10°.

Muzzle velocity was 1,250ft/sec (381m/s) when firing high-explosive anti-tank (HEAT) rounds with a separate bagged charge. The gun was able to penetrate 100mm of armour at 1,000 yards (915m). Other ammunition included impact-fused high-explosive (HE) and various types of smoke and chemical rounds; see Table 8, page 92.

ABOVE Annotated view showing the turret controls for the late 75mm M2 and 76mm M1 guns. *(Warehouse Collection)*

BELOW Annotated view showing the turret controls for the 105mm howitzer. *(Warehouse Collection)*

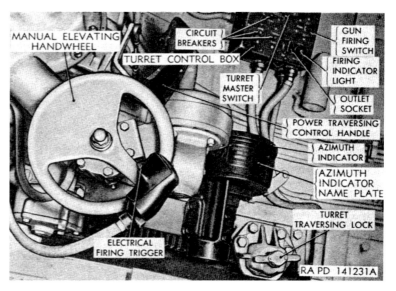

Table 8: Authorised ammunition for Sherman main gun

75mm M3 gun	Armour-piercing solid shot (AP). Armour-piercing capped (APC). Armour-piercing capped, ballistic cap (APCBC). Armour-piercing capped, with tracer (APC-T). Armour-piercing, with tracer (AP-T). Blank. Drill. High explosive (HE). High-explosive, with tracer (HEP-T). Hyper-velocity armour piercing (HVAP). Hyper-velocity armour piercing, with tracer (HVAP-T). Hyper-velocity target practice, with tracer (HVTP-T). Smoke, white phosphorus (WP).
76mm M1, M1A1, M1A1C, and M1A2 guns	Armour-piercing solid shot (AP). Armour-piercing capped (APC). Armour-piercing capped, with tracer (APC-T). Armour-piercing, with tracer (AP-T). Blank. Drill. High explosive (HE). High explosive, with tracer (HEP-T). Hyper-velocity armour piercing (HVAP). Hyper-velocity armour piercing, with tracer (HVAP-T). Hyper-velocity target practice, with tracer (HVTP-T). Smoke, white phosphorus (WP).
105mm M4 howitzer	Blank. Drill. High explosive (HE). High-explosive, with tracer (HEP-T). Illuminating. Mustard gas (H). Mustard gas, distilled (HD). Smoke, coloured (green, red, violet, yellow). Smoke, hexachlorethane mixture (HC). Smoke, sulphur trioxide in chlorosulphonic acid (FS). Smoke, white phosphorus (WP). Target practice, with tracer (TP-T).
17-pounder (76.2mm) Mk IV and Mk VII gun	Armour-piercing capped, ballistic-capped (APCBC). Armour-piercing discarding sabot (APDS). Blank. Drill. High explosive (HE).

Gyrostabiliser

All Shermans were fitted with a single-plane hydraulic gyrostabiliser on the gun mount that allowed the tank to fire on the move, albeit with restricted accuracy, by keeping the main gun and the co-axial machine gun at a predetermined elevation from the vertical. The technology was in its infancy and the likelihood of achieving a hit on the move was low. A US Army Field Manual of the period suggested that firing on the move was both inaccurate and wasteful of ammunition, stating that it should only be done in an emergency and then only if the range was less than 600 yards (550m). However, German tanks did not have this equipment, so that this was one small advantage enjoyed by the Sherman, and more than one Panzer commander was probably surprised when a Sherman gunner loosed off a shot without having to come to a halt... even if the chances were that he would miss!

Despite the Ordnance Board carrying out trials of a stabiliser that controlled both elevational and azimuth motions, the latter arising from the tank rolling or changing direction, the results were unsatisfactory. It wasn't until the post-war years that such equipment became sufficiently reliable to warrant its use.

Sighting and vision equipment

On early vehicles a single M6 driver's periscope was provided, giving forward vision only. The periscope consisted of two long prisms installed at each end of a metal housing; problems with internal condensation led to this being replaced in 1944 by the M13 prism, which was a solid block of plastic with a prism shape and a reflective surface moulded into each end. On later machines there was a second periscope that could be rotated through 360° and tilted to raise or lower the line of vision. Other crew members, except the gunner, were also provided with an M6 or M13 periscope.

The gunner's periscope was an M4, M4A1, M8A1, M10 or M16 design, incorporating a telescope with a ballistic reticule; the M10 and M16 periscopes incorporated two telescopes, one for close targets and the other for long-range work.

Towards the end of the production run an azimuth indicator was installed in the Sherman to assist with the accuracy of indirect fire.

Secondary weapons

The following secondary weapons were mounted:

- 0.50in M2 Browning heavy machine gun, in an anti-aircraft mount on the turret roof.
- 0.30in M1919A4 machine gun, co-axially mounted with the main gun and fired electrically via a solenoid.
- 0.30in M1919A4 machine gun, manually-operated by the co-driver and carried in a ball mount in the bow.
- 2in M3 smoke mortar launcher, facing forward in the turret (not fitted to all variants).
- 2in Mk I or IA bomb-thrower in the turret (Sherman Firefly).

A tripod was also carried to allow either of the 0.30in machine guns to be dismounted and fired from the ground.

Ammunition storage

Ammunition was originally carried in open racks in the side sponsons, beneath the gun and behind the co-driver's seat, with space for up to 97 rounds (104 in the M4A3E2) for the main gun in tanks with a welded hull, and 90 in the cast hulls; apparently tank crews quickly discovered that the racks also provided a perfect storage place for wine bottles! However, the ammunition proved vulnerable to fire if enemy hits penetrated the upper areas of the superstructure, and a short-term solution to this problem involved welding *appliqué* armour patches to the outer face of the side plates of the already welded hulls. A more satisfactory solution was the adoption of so-called 'wet' ammunition storage in 1944, when the ammunition was moved to water-protected racks below the turret.

Additional stowage was provided below the floor on tanks equipped with the 76mm gun. This necessitated cutting away most of the floor

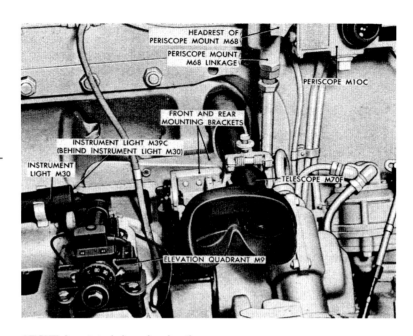

ABOVE Annotated view showing the gun-sighting and fire controls for the 75mm M2 gun.
(Warehouse Collection)

BELOW Annotated view showing the gun-sighting and fire controls for the 76mm M1 gun.
(Warehouse Collection)

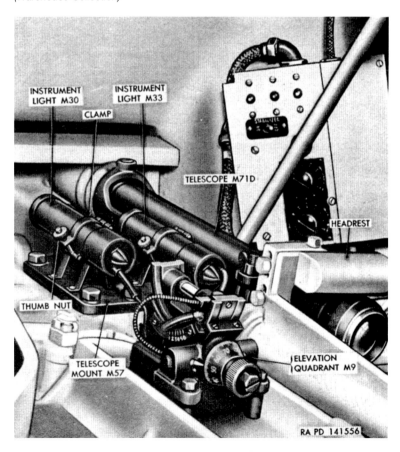

Table 9. Ammunition stowage

Variant:	M4		M4A1		M4A2		M4A3			M4A3E2	M4A4	M4A5	M4A6	Firefly VC
Main gun	*75mm*	*105mm*	*75mm*	*76mm*	*75mm*	*76mm*	*75mm**	*76mm*	*105mm*	*75mm*	*75mm*	*75mm*	*75mm*	*17-pounder*
Number of rounds carried														
Mounted weapons:														
Main gun	97	66	90	71	97	71	97	71	66	104	97	90	97	77
0.30in	4,750	4,000	4,750	6,250	4,750	6,250	4,750	6,250	4,000	6,250	4,750	4,750	4,750	5,000
0.50in	300	600	300	600	300	600	300	600	600	600	300	300	300	1,170
2in smoke bombs	12	12	-	12	12	14	12	18	15	18	–	–	12	27
Crew's personal weapons:														
0.45in	600	900	600	900	600	900	600	900	900	900	600	600	600	440
Hand grenades	12	12	12	12	12	12	12	12	12	12	12	12	12	9

* M4A3(75)W), with wet ammunition stowage: 104 main gun rounds, 6,250 x 0.30in machine-gun rounds, 600 x 0.50in machine-gun rounds, 18 x 2in smoke bombs.

of the turret basket, which as a bonus provided considerably more space in the fighting compartment.

See also Table 9, above.

Crew accommodation

Although at times it must have been a tight fit, especially when all of the hatches were closed-down, the Sherman was designed for a crew of five men – commander, gunner, loader, driver and co-driver/machine gunner – though some variants were routinely operated by a four-man crew. The interior was accessed via a hatch in the turret and two hatches at the front of the hull; there was also a small escape hatch in the hull floor.

Inside the hull, pedestal-mounted adjustable seats with removable backrests were provided for the driver, gunner and co-driver/machine gunner. The driver was placed at the front of the hull on the left, and the co-driver/machine gunner to his right; the gunner's seat was

ABOVE LEFT View inside a partially completed fighting compartment looking towards the rear, showing the driver's steering levers. *(Warehouse Collection)*

LEFT Interior view of the fighting compartment showing the driver's seat and the gearbox. Note the instrument panel just visible tucked away to the top left of the picture. *(Ian Young)*

attached to the floor of the turret basket. The driver could choose to operate the vehicle with the hatch open or closed, and during inclement weather a small hood and windscreen could be fitted to the sides of the hatch opening. Small seats for the commander and loader were provided in the turret, behind the gunner, and there was a second commander's seat in the upper part of the turret to allow him to ride with his upper body protruding through the hatch; in this position the commander had an excellent all-round view but, of course, was extremely vulnerable to enemy fire.

No regard was paid to what these days would be called passive safety. There were no restraining belts, and there were sharp-edged projections everywhere, designed to catch the unwary. Safety helmets of padded composite-fibre were issued to protect the crew but these were not popular, since they provided no ballistic protection, and many crews devised their own helmets instead, using the standard US Army steel pot helmet, with the liner removed, fitted over the tankers' padded helmet!

Communications equipment

The Sherman was equipped with an intercom system that allowed the crew members to communicate with one another via a throat microphone and headphones, the latter built into the protective helmet. A hand-held microphone was also available for the commander, and latterly an intercom extension kit was available that allowed the crew to communicate with infantry outside the tank via a handset carried in a box at the rear of the hull.

There was an official system of terse commands devised to standardise communications between crew members, but in the heat of battle the commands were often abbreviated, or abandoned altogether.

As regards tank-to-tank communications, or communications with brigade headquarters – and leaving aside determinedly 'low-tech' methods of communication such as bugles, pistol flares, messengers, field telephones, and signal flags (a set of which – in red, green and

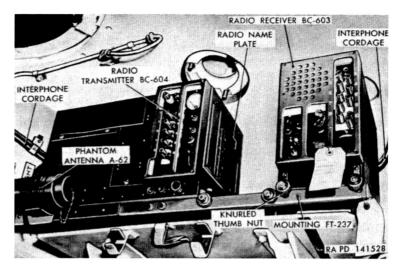

yellow – was carried in each tank), the US Army equipped its Shermans with an FM or AM radio set, installed in the turret bustle. Common FM sets included the SCR-508, SCR-528, SCR-538 and SCR-608B, each of which had a range of somewhere between five and 20 miles (8–32km) depending on local conditions, or the AM set AN/VRC-3. A command tank was often also equipped with an SCR-506, SCR-245 or SCR-193 in the right-hand sponson. The British and Canadian Armies used either the Number 19 or Number 29 set, both of them offering a range of up to 25 miles (40km).

At the time, a major disadvantage of using radio communication was the lack of security. It was easy enough for the enemy to either listen to or jam any transmissions.

ABOVE SCR-528 radio set installed on a shelf in the turret bustle (or 'overhang', in US Army parlance). Other suitable radio sets included the SCR-508, SCR-538, SCR-608B and AN/VRC-3. (Warehouse Collection)

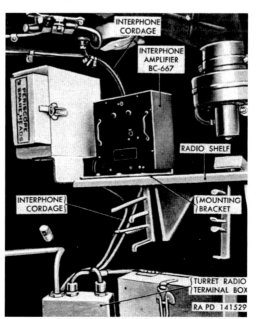

LEFT BC677 interphone amplifier installed in turret bustle. (Warehouse Collection)

Production changes and modifications

Aside from changes in construction, power plant and armament, many modest design amendments were made throughout the production life of the vehicle, either as a result of experience gained in the field or to simplify the manufacturing process. Many such changes were relatively minor, but there were two changes of sufficient significance to warrant special mention. The first of these was the move from the twin-hinged small hatch to a larger single-hinged hatch; the second was the change from the original vertical volute spring suspension system (VVSS) to the more robust horizontal volute spring suspension system (HVSS).

See Table 10, below, for a list – by no means comprehensive – of the changes made during production; note that not all of the changes were made to all tank variants.

Table 10: Changes to specification made during production

Hull and turret	1in (25mm) *appliqué* armour added to outside of hull to protect ammunition stowage areas. Addition of cupola to commander's hatch. Addition of loader's escape hatch. *Appliqué* armour added to vulnerable areas on outside of turret front. Elimination of pistol ports from turret... and subsequent reintroduction. Heavier nose casting (M4A3E2 only). Larger, counterbalanced hatch for driver and co-driver. Modification to shape of hull front (welded hulls only) and reduction in number of components. Provision for canvas dust screen around main gun shield (76mm gun only). Replacement of secondary cast hull components with welded fabrications. Replacement of three-piece bolted differential housing with one-piece cast housing. Split circular loader's hatch. Ventilation fan moved to centre of turret roof. Wet stowage facilities for ammunition; indicated by addition of 'W' suffix to numeric designation, *eg* M4A1(76)W.
Guns and sighting equipment	Addition of barrel clamp/lock for main gun. Addition of direct-sight telescope to M34 gun mount. Addition of smoke-bomb thrower. Introduction of metal vane sight for commander. Elimination of driver's bow-mounted 0.30in machine guns. Replacement of 0.50in turret machine gun with 0.30in weapon ... and subsequent reinstatement of 0.50in weapon. Replacement of M34 gun mount with later M34A1 design.
Engine, transmission and running gear	Addition of track grousers to reduce ground pressure. Addition of track sand screens. Adoption of upswept brackets for track return rollers. Change to final drive ratio (M4A3E2 only). Larger engine air filters. Modification to parking brake. Modification of track idler wheels. Modification of track return rollers. Modification of VVSS suspension system to increase longevity, including larger diameter springs. New designs of track, without rubber inserts. Replacement of VVSS suspension with heavier-duty HVSS system. Wider tracks (M4A3E8 only).
Secondary equipment	Addition of folding driver's rain hood. Addition of periscope guards. Deletion of external fuel shut-off valves. Elimination of driver's and co-driver's direct-vision slots in favour of secondary periscopes. Fixed headlights rather than removable lights. Siren moved to new position alongside left-hand headlight.

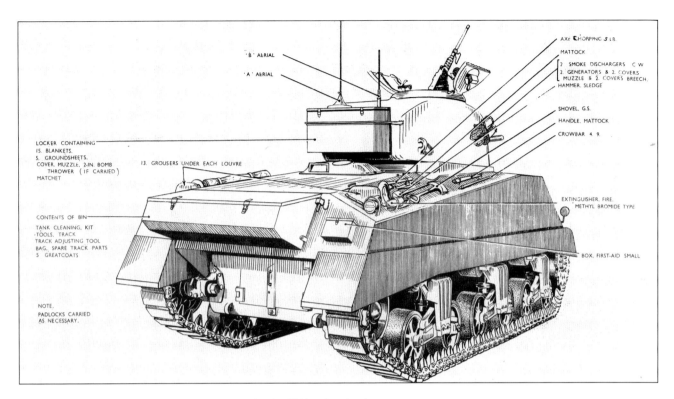

'B' AERIAL
'A' AERIAL

AXE CHOPPING 5 LB.
MATTOCK
{ 2 SMOKE DISCHARGERS C W
  2 GENERATORS & 2 COVERS
  MUZZLE & 2 COVERS BREECH.
HAMMER, SLEDGE
SHOVEL, G.S.
HANDLE, MATTOCK
CROWBAR 4 9.

LOCKER CONTAINING
15. BLANKETS.
5. GROUNDSHEETS.
COVER, MUZZLE, 2-IN. BOMB
    THROWER (IF CARRIED)
MATCHET

13. GROUSERS UNDER EACH LOUVRE

EXTINGUISHER, FIRE.
    METHYL BROMIDE TYPE

CONTENTS OF BIN
TANK CLEANING, KIT
TOOLS, TRACK
TRACK ADJUSTING TOOL
BAG, SPARE TRACK PARTS
5 GREATCOATS

BOX, FIRST-AID SMALL

NOTE.
PADLOCKS CARRIED
AS NECESSARY.

ABOVE British Army exterior stowage diagram for the M4A4 showing items carried on the right-hand side and the rear. *(Tank Museum)*

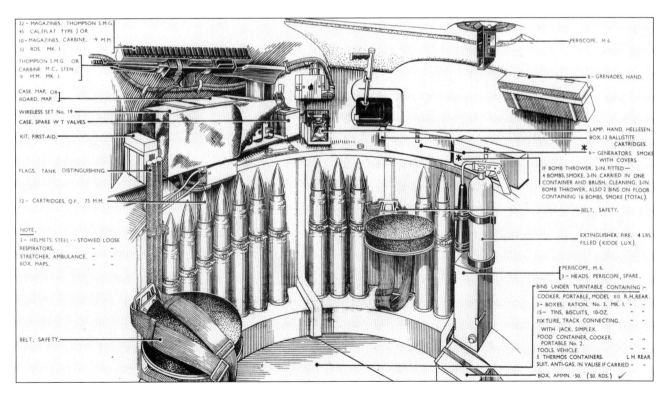

22 - MAGAZINES. THOMPSON S.M.G.
45 CAL.(FLAT TYPE) OR
10 - MAGAZINES. CARBINE. ·9 M.M.
.32 RDS. MK. I.

THOMPSON S.M.G. OR
CARBINE M.C. STEN
·9 M.M. MK. I.

CASE. MAP, OR
BOARD, MAP.

WIRELESS SET No. 19

CASE, SPARE W T VALVES.

KIT, FIRST-AID.

FLAGS, TANK DISTINGUISHING.

12 - CARTRIDGES, Q.F., 75 M.M.

NOTE.
3 - HELMETS, STEEL ·· STOWED LOOSE
RESPIRATORS,   "   "
STRETCHER, AMBULANCE,   "   "
BOX, MAPS.   "   "

BELT, SAFETY.

PERISCOPE. M 6.

6 - GRENADES, HAND.

LAMP, HAND, HELLESEN
BOX, 12 BALLISTITE
    CARTRIDGES.
6 - GENERATORS, SMOKE
    WITH COVERS
IF BOMB THROWER, 2-IN. FITTED —
4 BOMBS, SMOKE, 2-IN. CARRIED IN ONE
CONTAINER AND BRUSH, CLEANING, 2-IN.
BOMB THROWER, ALSO 2 BINS ON FLOOR
CONTAINING 16 BOMBS, SMOKE (TOTAL).

BELT, SAFETY.

EXTINGUISHER, FIRE. 4 LBS.
FILLED (KIDDE LUX).

PERISCOPE, M. 6.
3 - HEADS, PERISCOPE, SPARE.

BINS UNDER TURNTABLE CONTAINING :-
COOKER, PORTABLE, MODEL IIII R.H. REAR.
3 - BOXES, RATION, No. 3, MK. I.   "   "
15 - TINS, BISCUITS, 10-OZ.   "   "
FIXTURE, TRACK CONNECTING.   "   "
    WITH JACK, SIMPLEX.
FOOD CONTAINER, COOKER.   "   "
    PORTABLE No. 2.
TOOLS, VEHICLE.   "   "
5 THERMOS CONTAINERS.   L H. REAR
SUIT, ANTI-GAS, IN VALISE IF CARRIED "   "
BOX, AMMN. ·50. (50. RDS.)

ABOVE British Army internal stowage diagram for the M4A4 showing items carried inside the turret to the rear and on the left-hand side. *(Tank Museum)*

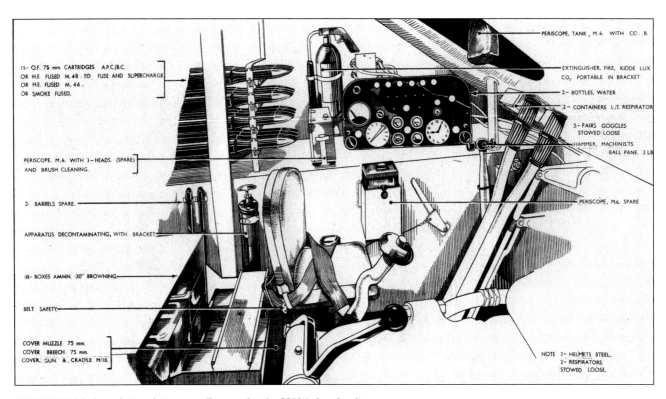

15- Q.F. 75 mm. CARTRIDGES A.P.C/B.C.
OR H.E. FUSED M.48 . P.D. FUSE AND SUPERCHARGE
OR H.E. FUSED M.46 .
OR SMOKE FUSED.

PERISCOPE, M.6. WITH 3-HEADS. (SPARE)
AND BRUSH CLEANING.

2- BARRELS SPARE.

APPARATUS. DECONTAMINATING, WITH. BRACKET.

18- BOXES AMMN. ·30" BROWNING.

BELT SAFETY.

COVER MUZZLE 75 mm.
COVER BREECH. 75 mm.
COVER. GUN & CRADLE M.10.

PERISCOPE, TANK , M.6. WITH CO.⋮R.

EXTINGUISHER, FIRE, KIDDE LUX
CO₂ PORTABLE IN BRACKET

2- BOTTLES, WATER

2- CONTAINERS L.T. RESPIRATOR

5- PAIRS GOGGLES
STOWED LOOSE

HAMMER, MACHINISTS
BALL PANE. 2 LB

PERISCOPE, M.6. SPARE

NOTE 2- HELMETS STEEL,
2- RESPIRATORS.
STOWED LOOSE.

ABOVE British Army internal stowage diagram for the M4A4 showing items carried in the left-hand side of the fighting compartment and in the driver's compartment. *(Tank Museum)*

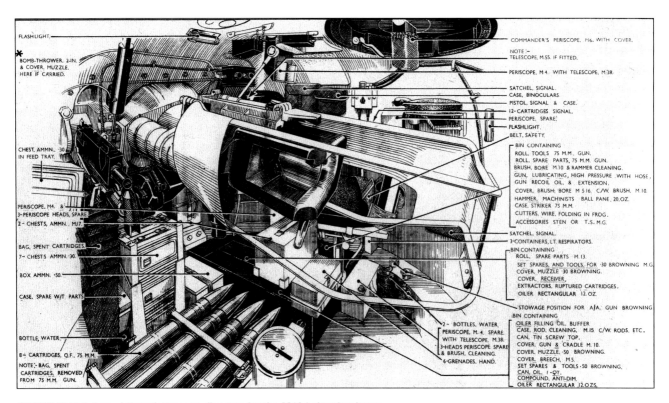

FLASHLIGHT.

✱ BOMB-THROWER. 2-IN.
& COVER, MUZZLE.
HERE IF CARRIED.

CHEST, AMMN., ·30
IN FEED TRAY.

PERISCOPE. M.4. &
3-PERISCOPE HEADS, SPARE
2 - CHESTS, AMMN. MJ7.

BAG, SPENT CARTRIDGES.
7- CHESTS AMMN. 30.

BOX AMMN. ·50.

CASE, SPARE W/T PARTS

BOTTLE, WATER.

8- CARTRIDGES, Q.F. 75 M.M.

NOTE:- BAG, SPENT
CARTRIDGES, REMOVED
FROM 75 M.M. GUN.

COMMANDER'S PERISCOPE, M.6, WITH COVER.

NOTE :-
TELESCOPE, M.55. IF FITTED.

PERISCOPE, M.4. WITH TELESCOPE, M.38.

SATCHEL, SIGNAL.
CASE, BINOCULARS.
PISTOL, SIGNAL & CASE.
12-CARTRIDGES SIGNAL,
PERISCOPE, SPARE.
FLASHLIGHT.
BELT, SAFETY.

BIN CONTAINING
ROLL, TOOLS 75 M.M. GUN.
ROLL, SPARE PARTS, 75 M.M. GUN.
BRUSH, BORE M.10 & RAMMER CLEANING.
GUN, LUBRICATING, HIGH PRESSURE WITH HOSE.
GUN RECOIL OIL, & EXTENSION.
COVER, BRUSH, BORE M 5.16. C/W. BRUSH, M.10.
HAMMER, MACHINISTS BALL PANE. 20.OZ.
CASE, STRIKER 75 M.M.
CUTTERS, WIRE, FOLDING IN FROG.
ACCESSORIES STEN OR T.S. M.G.

SATCHEL, SIGNAL.
3-CONTAINERS, L.T. RESPIRATORS.

BIN CONTAINING
ROLL, SPARE PARTS M.13.
SET SPARES, AND TOOLS, FOR ·30 BROWNING M.G.
COVER, MUZZLE ·30 BROWNING.
COVER, RECEIVER.
EXTRACTORS, RUPTURED CARTRIDGES.
OILER RECTANGULAR 12.OZ.

STOWAGE POSITION FOR A/A. GUN BROWNING

BIN CONTAINING
OILER FILLING OIL, BUFFER
CASE, ROD, CLEANING, M.15 C/W. RODS. ETC.
CAN, TIN SCREW TOP.
COVER, GUN & CRADLE M.10.
COVER, MUZZLE ·50 BROWNING.
COVER, BREECH, M.5.
SET SPARES & TOOLS ·50 BROWNING.
CAN, OIL, 1 -QT.
COMPOUND, ANTI-DIM.
OILER RECTANGULAR ,12.OZS.

2- BOTTLES, WATER.
PERISCOPE, M.4. SPARE.
WITH TELESCOPE, M.38.
3-HEADS PERISCOPE SPARE
& BRUSH. CLEANING.
6-GRENADES. HAND.

ABOVE British Army internal stowage diagram for the M4A4 showing items carried in the front of the turret. *(Tank Museum)*

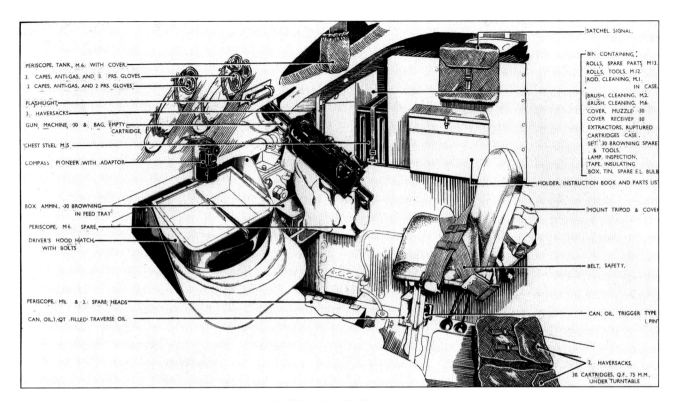

PERISCOPE, TANK, M.6. WITH COVER.
3. CAPES, ANTI-GAS, AND 3. PRS. GLOVES.
2. CAPES, ANTI-GAS, AND 2 PRS. GLOVES.
FLASHLIGHT.
3. HAVERSACKS.
GUN, MACHINE .30 &. BAG, EMPTY
CARTRIDGE.
CHEST STEEL M.5
COMPASS PIONEER WITH ADAPTOR

BOX AMMN., .30 BROWNING
IN FEED TRAY
PERISCOPE, M.6. SPARE.
DRIVER'S HOOD HATCH
WITH BOLTS

PERISCOPE, M.6. & .3. SPARE HEADS
CAN, OIL, 1 QT FILLED TRAVERSE OIL.

SATCHEL, SIGNAL.

BIN CONTAINING:
ROLLS, SPARE PARTS M.13.
ROLLS, TOOLS, M.12.
ROD, CLEANING, M.I.
IN CASE.
BRUSH, CLEANING, M.2.
BRUSH, CLEANING, M.6.
COVER, MUZZLE .30
COVER RECEIVER .30
EXTRACTORS, RUPTURED
CARTRIDGES CASE .
SET .30 BROWNING SPARE
& TOOLS.
LAMP, INSPECTION.
TAPE, INSULATING.
BOX, TIN, SPARE E.L. BULB.

HOLDER, INSTRUCTION BOOK AND PARTS LIST

MOUNT TRIPOD & COVER

BELT, SAFETY,

CAN, OIL, TRIGGER TYPE
1. PINT

2. HAVERSACKS,
30. CARTRIDGES, Q.F. 75 M.M.,
UNDER TURNTABLE

ABOVE British Army internal stowage diagram for the M4A4 showing items carried in the right-hand side of the fighting compartment and in the driver's compartment. *(Tank Museum)*

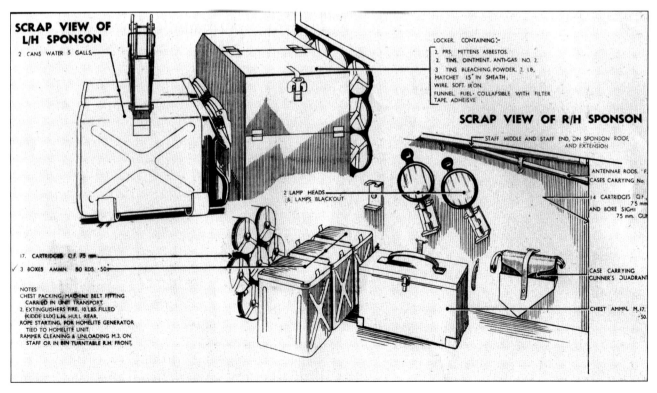

SCRAP VIEW OF L/H SPONSON
2 CANS WATER 5 GALLS.

LOCKER. CONTAINING:-
2. PRS. MITTENS ASBESTOS.
2. TINS. OINTMENT, ANTI-GAS NO. 2.
3 TINS BLEACHING POWDER, 2 LB,
MATCHET 15" IN SHEATH,
WIRE, SOFT. IRON.
FUNNEL, FUEL. COLLAPSIBLE WITH FILTER
TAPE, ADHESIVE

SCRAP VIEW OF R/H SPONSON
STAFF MIDDLE AND STAFF END, ON SPONSON ROOF
AND EXTENSION

ANTENNAE RODS. F.
CASES CARRYING No.

4 CARTRIDGES Q.F.
75 mm
AND BORE SIGHT
75 mm. GUN

2 LAMP HEADS
& LAMPS BLACKOUT

17. CARTRIDGES Q.F. 75 mm.
3 BOXES AMMN. 50 RDS. .50

CASE CARRYING
GUNNER'S QUADRANT

CHEST AMMN. M.17.
.50.

NOTES
CHEST PACKING, MACHINE BELT FITTING
CARRIED IN UNIT TRANSPORT.
2. EXTINGUISHERS FIRE, 10 LBS. FILLED
(KIDDE LUX) L.H. HULL REAR.
ROPE STARTING, FOR HOMELITE GENERATOR
TIED TO HOMELITE UNIT.
RAMMER CLEANING & UNLOADING M.3. ON
STAFF OR IN BIN TURNTABLE R.H. FRONT,

ABOVE British Army internal stowage diagram for the M4A4 (Sherman V) showing sundry items inside the hull. *(Tank Museum)*

'More than any other weapon of land warfare, the tank in World War Two captured the imagination of soldier and civilian alike. Its roaring motors, inscrutable armor and smoking guns added a new and terrifying element to the already grim life of the battlefield.'

US Army in World War II: the Ordnance Department: procurement and supply

The Sherman in action

The key doctrine for the deployment of US armoured forces was set out in field manual 'FM 100-5 Operations', where it was stated that 'the armored division is organized primarily to perform missions requiring great mobility and firepower... it is capable of engaging in all forms of combat, but its primary role is in offensive operations against hostile rear areas'. This suggests that medium tanks were intended to attack objectives such as artillery and supply depots, avoiding tank-on-tank action.

OPPOSITE US Army M4A3 75mm, with additional *appliqué* armour protecting the ammunition storage areas and the driver's and co-driver's hatch housings, passes a wrecked German tank. Note that the hatches are all open and that there is a crew member or infantryman riding on the hull behind the turret, which would suggest that the crew did not feel threatened. The censor has removed identifying marks from the vehicle. *(IWM, PL31235)*

Deployment

During World War Two Shermans fought in all of the major theatres, the first examples seeing action with the British 8th Army at the Second Battle of El Alamein in North Africa in October 1942. By the end of 1942 the US 2nd Armored Division had replaced the M3 Lee/ Grant with the Sherman, which was involved in 'Operation Torch', the invasion of French North Africa. The US 1st Armored Division was also subsequently re-equipped with Shermans and successfully fought in Tunisia. In addition US and British Army Shermans saw action in Belgium, France, Germany, Italy and Sicily, whilst US Shermans fought in the Pacific and Far East campaigns, where the Marines frequently deployed Shermans equipped with wading equipment to facilitate beach landings as they fought their way from one Pacific island to the next.

In North-West Europe, following the invasion of Normandy, Allied tanks almost always outnumbered those of the defenders – however, since the Sherman was comprehensively out-classed by the German Panther and Tiger tanks this was probably just as well, and it has been said that, statistically, it took between six and fifteen Shermans to destroy one Tiger. It should also perhaps be pointed out that the Germans built less than 6,000 Panthers, and that there were scarcely 1,400 Tigers and less

BELOW A US Army tank crew use their M4 to clear a burning *Wehrmacht* truck out of the road to allow a convoy of softskin vehicles to pass. The photograph is dated 29 March 1945, which would suggest that it was taken in Germany. *(Warehouse Collection)*

than 500 *Königstigers*, so the stark statistics do not tell the whole story. However, the German tanks weren't always outnumbered, and during the Battle of the Bulge the US Army fielded 1,320 Shermans against 1,800 German tanks, consisting of around 250 Tigers – of which most were of the Tiger I – variant, 775 *Panzer IVs* and 775 Panthers (*Panzer Vs*).

The Chinese successfully deployed 100 Shermans against the Japanese during 1943 and 1944, and the Red Army favoured the Sherman over the T-34 in certain situations. Even the German Army was not averse to fielding the odd captured Sherman.

Quantities of the M4A3E8 – the so-called 'Easy Eight' – were retained in service by the US Army after the end of World War Two and the type was a common sight in action during the Korean War, fighting alongside the M26 Pershing and M46 Patton, and often engaging the by now obsolete Soviet T-34. Although, on paper, the T-34 and the Sherman were more or less evenly matched, the Sherman's superior sighting and fire-control equipment normally provided sufficient edge to allow it to prevail. The US Army finally replaced the Sherman with Pattons during the 1950s and large numbers of ex-US Army Shermans were transferred to other friendly nations, where they enjoyed a second lease of life, often continuing to see action against the Soviet T-34, for example in the Arab-Israeli Wars in 1967 and 1973, the Chinese and Greek Civil Wars, and the First Indo-China War, as well as in the Indo-Pakistani Wars, where Shermans fought against Shermans.

Although a few specialised types remained in service with the British Army during the immediate post-war years – notably the Sherman-based beach armoured recovery vehicle (BARV) – the Sherman saw only brief service before it was replaced by the A41 Centurion.

Alongside Britain, Canada, the Soviet Union and the United States, the full list of nations deploying Shermans has included Argentina, Australia, Brazil, Chile, (People's Republic of) China, Cuba, Denmark, Egypt, France, India, Iran, Israel, Japan, Lebanon, Netherlands, New Zealand, Nicaragua, Pakistan, Paraguay, Peru, the Philippines, Poland, Portugal, Republic of China (Taiwan), Saudi Arabia, South Africa, South Korea, Turkey and Yugoslavia.

ABOVE Introduced in 1937, the German *PzKpfw III* tank remained in production until 1943 and was developed through various marks (*Ausf A* to *Ausf N*), with improvements to both the armour and the main gun. The example shown (*Ausf L*) has the long-barrelled 50mm *KwK 39* L/60 gun, which, despite lacking penetrative power, more or less matched the muzzle velocity of the Sherman's 76mm M1 gun.
(Warehouse Collection)

Crew

A s we have already seen, the Sherman was designed to be operated by a crew of five, consisting of a commander, driver, co-driver/ bow machine gunner, gunner and loader. However, a shortage of trained crew members sometimes saw them go into battle with as few as three men, with the commander doubling as loader, while in the Firefly the sheer size of the gun made it necessary to reduce the crew to four men, omitting the role of co-driver/bow machine gunner. The space inside the hull was always cramped, particularly with a five-man crew, and the day-to-day intimacy, coupled with the ever-present threat of death or serious injury, created a particular bond between crew members, who were forced to share everything in what could be their 'home' for weeks at a time. Generally the men ate, lived, slept and fought inside the tank, and in hot weather it was not uncommon for the crew to sleep in a hole that had been dug in the ground and then concealed by positioning the tank over it. It should surely be no surprise, therefore, that the men often came to regard one another as closer than family.

In the USA, at least, tank crews were generally drawn from amongst men who had some proven mechanical ability, but the actual training of crews was patchy, with some men apparently spending as long as two or even three years being prepared to face combat while others claimed that they were sent into battle after just 'a few hours' training. The US Army had established a series of service schools for training army ground forces, but although there were training courses for tank service crews there were initially no schools for tank crewmen, and their training consequently took place in units or replacement centres, which may explain the disparity. When the Armored Force Replacement Training Center (AFRTC) was established at Fort Knox, Kentucky, in 1940, the recruits were given two weeks of basic training before being selected for a specialism and passed on for further

LEFT The *PzKpfw VI Tiger* was the German tank that all Allied crews feared. Although the prototypes were armed with the 75mm *KwK 37* L/24 gun, by the time the Tiger went into production in 1942 in its *Ausf E* variant, the 75mm gun had been replaced by the fearsome 88mm *KwK 36* L/56 weapon... a gun that could outshoot both the 75mm and 76mm Shermans, and which was equalled only by the 17-pounder (76.2mm) gun of the British Sherman Firefly.
(Roland Groom, Tank Museum)

LEFT In January 1944 the Tiger I was joined by an even more formidable machine – the *PzKpfw VI Tiger II* or *Königstiger*. It is just as well that only 489 examples were produced, since the Allies had nothing that could match the penetrative power of its long-barrelled *KwK 43* L/71 gun, nor penetrate its 150mm frontal armour.
(Warehouse Collection)

training at the Armored Forces School (AFS). In Britain, Patton's Third Army spent some time training on Salisbury Plain before being committed to France.

Training often took place using M3/M5 Stuart light tanks, M3 Grant medium tanks and older variants of the M4 Sherman before the crews were let loose on battle-ready machines.

Roles

The commander was the senior crew member and was effectively in charge of the tank. His role was to locate likely targets and to determine the type of ammunition required to eliminate the threat; he was also expected to guide the gunner onto the target by voice command, and was responsible for co-ordinating his actions with other tanks in the platoon or troop. Next in seniority was the gunner. His task was, obviously, to aim and fire the main gun, but some gunners would first of all fire the co-axial machine gun at the target to confirm to the commander that the right target had been identified.

In combat the driver's role was to ensure that the tank was manoeuvred into the best position for engaging the target, whilst also ensuring that his own tank did not present an easy target itself. Whilst the commander was busy identifying suitable targets he would have little time to instruct the driver, and it helped greatly if the two men instinctively understood one another.

The loader, who was generally considered to be unskilled, was responsible for selecting the requested ammunition, either from a rack or from the floor where it had been placed ready for use;

LEFT Period colour photograph showing the laborious method of loading ammunition into the hull by hand; the mixed load for the 75mm gun consists of high-explosive super-charge (HE) and armour-piercing (AP) rounds. *(Warehouse Collection)*

putting the round inside the breech, which would usually have been opened immediately it was obvious that there was likely to be some kind of engagement; and unlatching the breechblock to allow it to close. The gunner was then ready to fire the gun, generally using the foot-operated solenoid switch. Once the round had been fired, the breech would automatically open, ejecting the previous spent round, ready for the loading operation to begin again. It was also the loader's task to aid the commander in the use of the radio.

The co-driver operated the bow machine gun, but would also often hand rounds to the loader from the forward ammunition bins.

As well as fighting, the crew were expected to maintain the tank in fighting condition: as the British Army put it in 'Army Book 413', published in 1944, 'it is the duty of all tank crews to maintain their vehicles at regular intervals, and to ensure no item is overlooked'. And a Sherman required attention from each crew member at the beginning and the end of every day, during any lulls in fighting, and at unscheduled stops during a day's operation. In addition, there were separate tasks to be carried out by the crew at weekly and monthly intervals, and at each 500, 1,000 and 3,000 miles (800km, 1,600km and 5,000km). The various tasks were identified by alpha-numeric codes, and a 'strict record' was to be kept of all maintenance carried out, with the record countersigned by the tank commander.

Evacuation of the crew

If the tank was hit, the commander would give the order to evacuate and he would exit first through the turret hatch, followed by the gunner and then the loader; the driver and co-driver had their own escape hatches located in the bow of the tank. The hatches were small, but it is surprising how agile a man becomes when he suddenly finds himself inside a burning tank!

There was also an emergency escape hatch in the floor.

Fighting with the Sherman

Following a major reorganisation in 1943 the US Army maintained two types of tank battalion: those belonging to the armoured divisions, each of which had three or six

ABOVE Composite-hull M4 75mm photographed 'somewhere in England' in May 1944. Although never universally adopted, the white stripe around the turret was applied for identification purposes and was supposed to reduce the likelihood of friendly fire incidents. *(Tank Museum)*

LEFT Chrysler-engined M4A4 75mm, probably of the Free French Army, positioned for a spot of street fighting. Note the Allied recognition star on the turret roof. *(Warehouse Collection)*

LEFT Welded-hull M4 75mm carrying spare track links and bogie wheels on the glacis plate; whilst this was a useful place to store spare components, many crews also believed that the track links, particularly, provided some measure of additional protection. Note the smoke launchers on the side of the turret. *(Tank Museum)*

LEFT Photographed during training in August 1944, this GM Detroit Diesel-engined M4A2 belongs to the Canadian Army. The front and rear sections of the track guards have been removed. *(Tank Museum)*

BELOW British Army M4A1 75mm DD Shermans passing through a French town on their way to the front line (25 June 1944). The wading screens have been removed completely, leaving just the perimeter support around the hull. *(IWM, B5897)*

BELOW US troops using a Sherman as cover; note the Culin hedgerow cutter installed on the nose of the tank. The photograph was taken in Belgium in September 1944. *(Tank Museum)*

RIGHT German prisoners standing knee-deep in the sea at Hermanville-sur-Mer (Sword Beach) in front of a Sherman Crab mine flail that would appear to be disabled. Note the wading duct still in place on the tank. *(IWM, B5089)*

BELOW British Army Sherman beach armoured recovery vehicle (BARV) rescuing a Bedford OW truck that had become drowned or bogged-down on the beach. The armoured extensions to the hull allowed the BARV to operate in up to eight feet (2.4m) of water. *(IWM, B5578)*

battalions, and the independent tank battalions that were designed to support the infantry. It was a similar story in the British Army, where domestic tanks were described as either 'cruiser' or 'infantry' tanks according to their role; the Sherman was considered to be an infantry tank.

The method of deployment for US armoured forces at the time was set out in the field manual 'FM 100-5 Operations'. In the 1941 edition of this document, which in its current edition remains the authoritative guide on all aspects of how the US armed forces set about the business of warfare, it was explicitly stated (paragraph 1072) that 'the armored division is organized primarily to perform missions that require great mobility and firepower... it is given decisive missions... it is capable of engaging

LEFT US Army M4 75mm photographed advancing through Aachen in North Rhine-Westphalia, October 1944. *(Tank Museum)*

BELOW A pair of US Army M4A3 75mm Shermans advancing in single file. The second tank has eyes painted on the gun mantlet, which would suggest that the photograph was taken in the Far East. *(Tank Museum)*

in all forms of combat, but its primary role is in offensive operations against hostile rear areas'. What this meant was that the medium (and the earlier light) tanks, which were operated by the armoured divisions, were not intended to engage opposing enemy armour, but were expected to be used to attack objectives in the rear such as artillery and supply depots. The role of the Sherman M4 medium tank, specifically, was covered by 'FM 17-33 The tank battalion, light and medium', dated September 1942, which devoted just one page of text and four diagrams to what might be described as tank-on-tank action. This may seem odd, but

surprisingly it has been reported that US Army tanks spent only around 15% of their combat time engaged with enemy armour. Unfortunately when this situation did arise, the Sherman – although not as tall as the M3 medium tank which it replaced – provided a temptingly prominent silhouette for the enemy gunners, one British tank crew member reflecting soberly that 'it was too big' for his liking and that 'Jerry wouldn't have much trouble hitting it'.

In theory, then, it was only the heavy tanks and tank destroyers that were intended to break through fortified lines; but of course, in wartime things have a habit of not always working out as planned. Heavy US tanks, in the form of the M26 Pershing, were not available in Europe in large numbers, and anyway did not appear until the spring of 1945, and for some reason the *Wehrmacht* was not inclined to follow US Armored Force doctrine anyway! This meant that Shermans frequently found themselves facing the more powerful German machines, a role for which they were not well suited, since neither the 75mm nor 76mm guns of the standard Sherman had much hope of defeating the frontal armour of the heavier German tanks. The disparity in performance between the Allied and German tanks often led to shortages of Shermans during the heavy fighting in the Normandy *bocage* country, where it proved difficult and hazardous for the Allied tanks to break through the dense hedgerows. During this fighting in June and July 1944, the US 1st Army alone lost 467 of 1,153 medium tanks. It was not until a US Army sergeant named Curtis G. Culin developed a fabricated steel device designed to be attached to the front of the tanks to uproot hedgerows that real progress was made; tanks that were equipped with this device were described as either Rhinoceros or Prong.

As the war progressed, and particularly during the battle for Normandy in 1944, many Allied tank crews began to believe that their Shermans were always outclassed by the German tanks, regardless of the particular variant that was encountered. This was not necessarily the case – for example, the *Panzer II* and *Panzer III*, which were certainly still in service into 1943, were both inferior to the Sherman in every respect, whilst the *Panzer IV* was more or less equal in most respects. When it came to the *Panzer V* (Panther) and the *Panzer VI* (Tiger and *Königstiger*), it was, perhaps, a different matter, with all three designs generally proving themselves to be superior to the Sherman in combat, and all Sherman crews lived in constant fear of unexpectedly encountering a Tiger.

The later German tanks were capable of knocking out a Sherman at ranges from 1,000 to 1,500 yards (985–1,475m) greater than those at which the Sherman was effective; in fact, a Sherman could often be picked off by a Tiger before the Allied crew even realised that it was a target. It was only the Sherman VC Firefly, equipped with the British 17-pounder (76.2mm) gun, that had any realistic hope of dealing with the heavier German tanks. That is not to say that the 75mm and 76mm guns were not capable of getting the odd lucky shot; in July 1944 a British 75mm Sherman managed to

destroy a Panther at 800 yards (730m) head-on, the round penetrating downwards through the mantlet and the plate covering the driver's and wireless operator's compartment. One advantage that the Sherman had was in its speed of traverse; the long 75mm gun on the Panther made the turret heavy and slow, often allowing the Sherman to fire one or more shots whilst the German was still struggling to turn its turret towards the target.

Engagement with the enemy

When engaging an enemy tank the standard operating procedure (SOP) for Patton's Third

ABOVE During the battle for Normandy the Allied tanks had great difficulty in breaking through the hedgerows that lined the sunken roads of the area. Tanks that were able to break through presented their vulnerable floor area, which was just 25mm thick, to enemy fire. Although not photographed in Normandy, this cast-hull M4A1 demonstrates its vulnerable areas. *(Warehouse Collection)*

BELOW The tall wading ducts installed over the air-intake vents, and sometimes the exhaust pipes, at the rear of the Sherman allowed it to undertake amphibious crossings, driving on the river bed or beach rather than floating. *(Tank Museum)*

ABOVE A US Army sergeant named Curtis G. Culin III developed a fabricated steel device that could be attached to the front of a tank to uproot the Normandy hedgerows. The four-pronged plough was constructed using the remnants of German anti-tank defences salvaged from the Normandy beaches, and tanks that were equipped with the device were described as either Rhinoceros or Prong. The photograph shows an M3/M5 Stuart light tank, but the device was equally applicable to the M4 Sherman. *(Warehouse Collection)*

Army was firstly to fire an armour-piercing round (AP), and during training gunners were impressed with the importance of getting a hit with the first shot against surprise targets. If the first shot missed or failed to disable the enemy, it was common practice to fire a smoke round which would allow the attacking tank to manoeuvre to a different position under cover of the smoke whilst keeping the gun laid on the original target. This allowed a second shot to be made on the enemy tank from a different position, thus recovering some of the element of surprise.

The Royal Scots Greys tried to avoid giving the enemy the opportunity to take a long-range 'sitting shot' and, where possible, engaged the German tank(s) across a short field of fire, round about 600 to 800 yards (550–730m). Since the Germans quickly learned of the lethality and importance of the Fireflys, the Scots Greys also tried to ensure that all of the tanks in a troop opened fire at once, thus making it more difficult for the enemy to locate which was the Firefly.

Some tank crews firing the 75mm and 76mm guns preferred to use high-explosive (HE) rounds, sometimes with a delay fuse set

to 'superquick', before changing to armour-piercing. In this way they could perhaps disable the German tank by breaking a track – which of course did not render the gun inoperable – or by jamming the turret. Alternatively, by positioning themselves for a side shot it was possible to penetrate the thinner areas on the German hull. It was also possible to fire the gun in an indirect mode rather like an artillery piece, although the lack of sufficient elevation made this rather less than successful, and required co-ordination from a 'forward observation officer' (FOO). Finally, if all else failed, artillery fire could be called down on the enemy tanks, since an overhead shot could penetrate the thinner roof or engine covers of the German machines.

By contrast, in the Pacific theatre a Sherman was always more than capable of dealing with the lighter Japanese armour. As an example, the CHI-HA medium tank was considered the best Japanese AFV of World War Two, and this was equipped only with a 47mm or 57mm gun, and nowhere did the thickness of the hull exceed 26mm; the only Japanese armoured vehicle that stood any real chance of knocking

ABOVE Photographed during a training exercise, these Free French troops are loading ammunition into an M4 75mm, passing it from hand to hand. The rounds are high-explosive with an impact fuse. *(Tank Museum)*

BELOW Line-up of Canadian Shermans at a victory parade on 23 May 1945. Note how the larger-gunned Fireflys alternate with tanks fitted with the original 75mm gun. *(Warehouse Collection)*

out a Sherman was the HO-NI medium self-propelled gun, fitted with a 75mm weapon.

During combat, conditions inside the tank would gradually become less and less pleasant. Spent shell cases would pile up on the floor of the turret basket, eventually to be ejected manually through the roof hatch or the turret pistol port, and, despite the extract ventilators, any period of sustained firing – particularly if both the main gun and one of the machine guns were in use – quickly resulted in an unpleasant accumulation of cordite fumes inside the hull and turret.

American vs German tank guns

The power and effectiveness of any weapon are functions of the calibre, barrel length, type and size of round, the size of the charge and the resulting muzzle velocity, but tactics and opportunity often play an equally significant

role... not to mention getting in the first shot. However, it should also be remembered that tanks rarely face one another down in a straight one-on-one shoot-out like Western gunslingers, so the bald figures relating to firepower and armoured protection (see Table 7, page 88) are not necessarily a reliable measure of the performance of the tank in combat.

However, it would generally be fair to say that the 75mm gun of the early Sherman, and its 76mm replacement, were both well matched to the 37mm and 50mm guns of the Panzer III on a directly comparable basis. It was only with the later German developments that Allied crews found themselves at a real disadvantage, lacking both the range and penetrative power of the powerful German 75mm and 88mm guns, and without the same degree of armoured protection; unless fired at point-blank range, US 75mm and 76mm guns

generally failed to penetrate the massive frontal armour of the Panther, Tiger and *Königstiger*, whilst the German guns were sufficiently powerful to be able to penetrate a Sherman at long range. In one instance two Shermans are said to have been knocked out by a single anti-tank round, which passed through the first tank and penetrated the second.

As has been stated already, only the 17-pounder (76.2mm) equipped Firefly put the German and Allied tank guns on a more or less equal footing. A document prepared by the Brigadier Commander of the Royal Scots Greys in late July 1944 stated categorically that 'before our arrival in France it was expected that encounters with Marks V and VI German tanks would be the exception rather than the rule; consequently the 75mm Sherman which had dealt adequately with any German tank or self-propelled gun we had met in the desert or Italy was regarded as the basic tank in the squadron. Experience has now shown that there are few occasions on which German tanks are met when Mark V or VI tanks are not present; the 75mm Sherman is at a definite disadvantage when compared to these... consequently for tank-versus-tank purposes the Sherman VC Firefly is [now considered to be] the basic tank in the squadron.'

Similarly, in August 1944 the US 12th Army Group commander requested that 'theatre headquarters' take immediate action to convert sufficient Shermans to Firefly configuration to provide one 17-pounder (76.2mm) for each medium tank platoon engaged in North-West Europe. Nothing came of this request, since it would have meant withdrawing tanks from the often meagre reserves to facilitate the conversions

ABOVE The US Army's M26 TR-1 'Dragon Wagon' was an armoured tank transporter tractor designed to be coupled to a Fruehauf 45-ton semi-trailer unit to produce the 'truck-trailer, 45-ton, tank transporter, M25'. The load is a Sherman M4 equipped for wading. (Tank Museum)

RIGHT The softskin variant of the 'Dragon Wagon' tank transporter train, seen here carrying a Sherman M32B1 armoured recovery vehicle, was designated M26A1. (Warehouse Collection)

Table 11:
Main characteristics of Allied and German tank guns

Gun	Application	Muzzle velocity:		Maximum penetration at 1,000yd (910m)*	Ammunition type†
		ft/sec	m/s		
US tank guns					
75mm M2 L/31.1	M4A1	1,930	590	62mm	APCBC
75mm M3 L/40.1	M4, M4A1 to A6	2,030	619	59mm	APC
76mm M1A1, M1A2	M4A1 to A3	2,600	793	89mm	APCBC
76mm M1A1, M1A2	M4A1 to A3	3,400	1,037	134mm	HVAP
105mm M4	M4, M4A3	1,250	381	100mm	HEAT
British tank guns					
17-pounder (76.2mm)	M4 Firefly	2,900	885	118mm	APCBC
17-pounder (76.2mm)	M4 Firefly	3,950	1,205	170mm	APDS
German tank guns					
37mm L/46.5	*PzKpfw III A to D*	2,445	745	30mm (at 500 yards)	APC
37mm L/46.5	*PzKpfw III A to D*	3,450	1,052	22mm	APCR
50mm L/42 'short'	*PzKpfw III E to J*	2,250	686	47mm	APC
50mm L/42 'short'	*PzKpfw III E to J*	3,445	1,050	42mm	APCR
50mm L/60 'long'	*PzKpfw III J, L*	2,700	824	50mm	APC
50mm L/60 'long'	*PzKpfw III J, L*	3,930	1,199	55mm	APCR
75mm L/24 'short'	*PzKpfw III N*	1,260	384	41mm	APCBC
75mm L/24 'short'	*PzKpfw IV A to F1*	1,450	442	43mm	HEAT
75mm L/40 'long'	*PzKpfw IV F2 to H*	2,300	702	72mm	APCBC
75mm L/40 'long'	*PzKpfw IV F2 to H*	2,450	747	79mm	APCBC
75mm L/70	*PzKpfw V Panther*	3,070	936	121mm	APCBC
88mm L/56	*PzKpfw VI Tiger I*	2,660	811	101mm	APCBC
88mm L/56	*PzKpfw VI Tiger I*	3,070	936	103mm	APCR
88mm L/71	*PzKpfw VI Tiger II*	3,340	1,019	167mm	APCBC

* Maximum effective range given; actual figure depends on type of ammunition in use.
† APC, armour-piercing capped; APCBC, armour-piercing capped, ballistic cap; APCR, armour-piercing capped, rigid; HVAP, hyper-velocity armour-piercing (also described as high-velocity armour-piercing); APDS, armour-piercing discarding sabot; HEAT, high-explosive anti-tank; hyper-velocity (or high-velocity) armour-piercing. A 'T' suffix, *eg* HVAP-T, indicates that a particular ammunition type includes phosphorus to provide a tracer facility.

Armoured protection

The Sherman had the advantage of being better armoured than the early German tanks, with 50 to 65mm of armour on the hull front and 75 to 90mm on the turret face, but was vulnerable to penetration by the later 75mm and 88mm German tank guns, and to Teller mines, which the Germans would occasionally stack one on top of the other to increase the blast effect. Most areas of the Sherman hull could also be defeated by infantry anti-tank weapons such as the disposable *Panzerfaust* 60 and 100, which could penetrate 200mm and 220mm of armour from a range of 65 yards (60m) and 109 yards (100m) respectively. One trick used by the *Wehrmacht* during street battles, particularly during the hard-fought battle for Germany in the closing months of the war, was to fire a *Panzerfaust* down on to the lightly-armoured roof or engine cover of a Sherman from the upper floor of a building. And if a *Panzerfaust* was not to hand a Molotov cocktail lobbed down in the same way could often be relied upon to set the tank on fire.

The story was much the same with artillery, with the thinner armour of the Sherman proving especially vulnerable to the larger German guns. A 155mm round could create havoc inside a Sherman even after striking the thickest area of the hull, and a frontal shot was well able to penetrate either the glacis plate or the differential housing and the transmission.

German tank armour

As regards the German tanks that a Sherman was likely to engage, the frontal hull armour on both the *Panzer III* and the *Panzer IV* was 30 to 50mm, with 30 to 57mm on the turret face. The later *Panzer V* (Panther) was considerably better armoured, with up to 120mm of armour on the turret and 60 to 80mm on the hull. However, all Allied crews feared an encounter with the formidable *Panzer VI* (Tiger) and the later *Königstiger*, and for good reason. Frontal armour on the Tiger was a maximum of 100mm on both the hull and the turret face, and on the later *Königstiger* the thickness was increased to 180mm on the turret face, with a maximum of 100mm on the hull.

This disparity of armour was a serious issue, and there were enough stories – some perhaps apocryphal – of Allied anti-tank rounds simply 'bouncing off' the later German tanks to lead to questions being asked in Congress regarding the effectiveness of the US Army's tank guns.

Battle damage

The experience of being inside a tank that is under attack cannot be pleasant. Machine-gun fire against the hull creates a rattling sound, which must be very unnerving, whilst a direct hit from either an anti-tank round or a *Panzerfaust* which fails to penetrate the armour would create what has been described, with typical British understatement, as 'a terrific thud' or 'a hell of a crack', accompanied by showers of dust and loose material from inside the hull. Even rounds that had insufficient velocity to cause any real damage would cause the tank to rock on its suspension, and there would be localised heating of the hull at the point of impact, created by the kinetic energy of the incoming round being converted to heat energy, which would inevitably be accompanied by spalling of hot particles of metal from the inner face. Buttoned-down and unable to see much of what was going on the crew would, inevitably, be wondering whether or not the next round might penetrate the armour, and one can only imagine the conditions inside the tank.

A round that penetrated the hull but did not pass right through would result in a shower of molten metal particles inside, which, aside from its devastating effect on the crew, could well short-out electrical equipment and start a fire... and, of course, the projectile itself remained extremely hot to the touch. Surviving Sherman crews often tell stories of rounds that penetrated the hull and passed right through, often killing or injuring one crewman whilst leaving the others unscathed.

Fire was an ever-present threat, and it has been said that nine out of ten Shermans would 'brew-up', as the crews described it, when hit. A fire often resulted from penetration of the fuel tanks, or a direct hit on the engine or, more likely, the ammunition storage racks. In fact the Sherman quickly acquired a reputation for catching fire, leading to the Germans referring to them as 'Tommy Cookers'. Even the US crews described them as 'Ronsons'! At night, following a tank-on-tank engagement, it was apparently possible to see the still-glowing hulks of burned-out tanks littering the battlefield.

The tank was equipped with a fire-extinguishing system, but this was operated manually, and if the crew was injured or incapacitated there might not have been time to trigger the extinguishers. Any fire would quickly become established and burn out of control, particularly if the cupola or any of the hatches were open. A tank which has completely burned out was generally considered to be fit only for scrap, since the heat of the fire would destroy the hardening of the armour, and in any case, internal explosions would frequently destroy the hull. A damaged turret or gun mount could be replaced, but any hit that distorted the turret ring would render the tank unrepairable.

Anti-tank mines had the capacity to distort the bottom plate of the hull and to break tracks or destroy suspension units to the point where the hull was beyond repair. Even an anti-personnel mine could break a track, rendering the tank immobile... and, of course, an immobile tank is a sitting duck for the enemy.

Repair

Badly-damaged US tanks were either recovered and repaired in the field or, if the damage was too severe but the tank was still judged to be repairable, it would be returned to an Ordnance Depot. In this instance the fighting unit that had 'lost' the tank would be issued with a replacement, either a new, factory-fresh machine or a tank that had been repaired; but tank crews were often very superstitious about being given a tank which had been repaired, particularly if the hull had been penetrated.

Although the practice ran counter to the original US Army procedures, which assumed a low rate of tank casualties and a plentiful supply of parts, badly damaged tanks were frequently cannibalised for parts to keep others running.

Post-war users

By the end of the World War Two the new threat to the West came from the Soviet Union, and there is little doubt that the Sherman was outclassed by the heavier Soviet armour. The US Army retained many of its Shermans for a decade or so, with some even seeing further fighting in Korea, but it was gradually replaced by the heavier M26 Pershing and the M46/M47 Patton. Similarly, in Britain the Shermans were fairly quickly replaced by the Centurion. Canada abandoned all of its Shermans in Europe at the end of the war, donating them to the armies of Belgium and the Netherlands.

An article in the British Army's *Soldier* magazine of November 1953, headed 'What am I bid for 50 Shermans?', described how this quantity of derelict petrol-engined Shermans – the property of Rotinoff Construction Limited since their original disposal in 1945 – was being auctioned as surplus to requirements at the company's yard at Poyle, Buckinghamshire. The tanks had originally been purchased to provide parts for the diesel-engined Shermans that Rotinoff had been converting to tractors, and having yielded whatever was useful were now being sold at scrap value. All of the bidders were metal merchants, and the auctioneer announced that they would have eight weeks to dismantle the tanks on site. However, most bidders said that even at £4 a ton there was too much work involved in cutting-up the tanks for scrap and there would be little profit in it. Nevertheless, the prices peaked at a surprising £480 each for a pair of reconditioned machines, with lesser machines selling at £250, and then just £140 (£9,980–£2,910 at 2011 prices). The sale also included some power units, with Continental engines selling at up to £40 each, and Chrysler multi-banks at £19. It seems that whilst there was no profit in the scrap value of the steel, there was a ready market for spare parts to be sold to foreign governments.

Clearly, the Sherman was by no means finished when Germany and then Japan surrendered, and surplus tanks ended up serving with the armies of Argentina, Chile, Egypt, France, India, Indonesia, Israel, Japan, Mexico, Nicaragua, Pakistan, the Philippines, Syria, Uganda and maybe elsewhere. Shermans fought on both sides during the Indo-Pakistan War of 1965, and the type saw action in the Arab-Israeli wars, in Suez, in

Cuba, and as late as 1990 some examples took part in the Lebanese Civil War.

Civilian uses

Believe it or not, surplus Shermans also found more than a few civilian uses, both in the USA and around the world.

Established in 1951, the Southeastern Equipment Company (SECO), based in Augusta, Georgia, specialised in converting redundant tanks into tracked vehicles for the logging industry. The company purchased around 50 Grizzly-based Sexton 25-pounder self-propelled guns from Portugal in the early 1980s for this purpose, and continues to supply and service military vehicles to this day. In British Columbia, Canada, Madill Equipment and Morgan Power Apparatus (Morpac) both converted Sherman hulls into off-road crawlers and logging tractors, and in the Soviet Union a number were converted to heavy tractors for reconstructing railway lines.

In Britain, Shermans were converted to agricultural tractors by Vickers-Armstrong, and were marketed to West Africa as logging tractors under the name Shervick. Also in Britain, a number of Shermans were employed in open-cast coal mining and, as already mentioned, the British company Rotinoff Construction converted a number of M4A2 Shermans into tracked 'dozers, while in South Africa turretless Shermans were rebuilt as heavy tractors under the name Rotrac.

ABOVE Produced by Vickers, the Shervick was a heavy-duty logging tractor based on a heavily-modified Sherman hull; note how the hull has been shortened and reversed to place the engine at the front. *(Tank Museum)*

BELOW In South Africa, a Cape Town-based company rebuilt a number of turretless Shermans as heavy tractors under the name Rotrac. *(Stuart Gibbard)*

BELOW The Poyle-based British company Rotinoff also undertook the conversion of diesel-engined M4A2 Shermans to produce a heavy 'dozer-equipped tractor. *(Warehouse Collection)*

LEFT In 1953 Rotinoff auctioned the remains of 50 Shermans that had originally been purchased as donor vehicles to assist in the tractor-conversion programme. The tanks were offered at scrap value and most had already had their gun barrels destroyed. *(Warehouse Collection)*

'Did you hear I bought a tank?'
'Oh, really? Where do you park it?'
'Wherever the hell I like!'
Anon

Chapter Six

Owning a Sherman

Make no mistake, owning a tank is a rich man's pastime. Having shelled out the thick end of a quarter of a million pounds to buy the thing, the running costs are considerable... a low-loader will be required to get the vehicle to an event, and refuelling will never be a simple matter of popping down to the local service station; rather, the service station will need to be brought to the tank; and with a capacity of around 175 US gallons (146 imperial gallons, 661 litres) for a range between 75 and 130 miles (121–210km), the bill will be considerable!

OPPOSITE The lengths to which some enthusiasts are prepared to go in pursuit of their hobby are considerable. Consider this beautifully restored Chrysler-engined M4A4 that was shipped by ferry and train to Normandy to participate in the 2004 events to commemorate the D-Day landings. *(Ian Young)*

119

Despite the many difficulties associated with buying, storing, running and maintaining such a machine, tank ownership is seen by many military vehicle collectors as the pinnacle of the hobby. On the other hand, those who might never have considered such a thing even possible will, almost certainly, walk away from the hapless tank owner shaking their head in disbelief. But there is something very special about the sight and sound of a tank on the move, the mighty roar of the huge engines combining with the distinctive squeak and rhythmic clatter of the tracks to create a unique automotive soundtrack, every bit as addictive as more conventional motoring exotica.

As with so many fields of collecting, there is an inevitable hierarchy. Entry-level machines in the world of military vehicle collecting include surplus Land Rovers; given a little more money the keen enthusiast may graduate to a Jeep or a larger truck. For those who graduate from soft-skin vehicles to armour, post-war British tanks remain relatively affordable, whilst at the other end of the scale German armour from World War Two should be considered to be virtually unavailable. However, for those who absolutely must have a World War Two tank, serious collectors have turned to the Allied tanks that helped to defeat the Nazi war machine, and of these the Sherman is undoubtedly the most iconic, even if it is not the most affordable.

Despite having survived in relatively large numbers, prices have risen inexorably to the point where a well-restored Sherman is likely to cost upwards of a quarter of a million pounds, and for many who have set their heart on owning such a machine it might be sensible to consider becoming, or forming, a joint ownership group. It wasn't always thus, and surplus Shermans were once priced at little more than their scrap value. In 1947, a Lincolnshire farmer, Robert Crawford, actually converted an M4A4 Chrysler multi-bank-engined Sherman for ploughing, firstly with the turret removed, and later with the entire upper hull cut off. It was used in this form until 1957, and the orange-painted machine

has subsequently been restored, providing an awesome sight at enthusiasts' ploughing matches and demonstrations in the area.

But most restored Shermans are now in the hands of museums and military vehicle enthusiasts – and it is as well to remember that the expense does not end when the cheque has been cleared.

There are problems associated with private ownership of a tank that are not apparent with more practical classic machinery. Not least of these is the cost of fuel and the appetite with which the vehicle consumes it. There is also the question of transportation, and the fact that any breakdown that incapacitates the vehicle to an extent where recovery is required will be expensive and will present a considerable logistical challenge. 'Roadside' repairs are generally impossible without a very well equipped support team.

Buying a Sherman

Although a surprising number of Shermans have survived, with the total almost certainly in the order of hundreds, anyone searching for an example to buy is not going to be spoilt for choice, since at any given moment there are unlikely to be more than three or four examples for sale. However, unlike the German Tiger, for which the number of examples can be counted on the fingers of one hand, sufficient numbers of Shermans change hands for there to be some kind of established market price. Admittedly, many are in museums, or serving as static monuments to those who helped to liberate Europe, but there are plenty of Shermans in the hands of collectors.

Nevertheless, if you have set your heart on owning a Sherman, the scarcity of suitable vehicles for sale means that locating a specific model to purchase will be time-consuming.

With only 75 examples constructed, the scarcest of the variants is the Caterpillar diesel-engined M4A6, and it may well be that none of these has survived at all; surprisingly, considering that just 188 were built, the Canadian M4A5 Grizzly is relatively numerous. At the other end of the scale, the most common variant to be found in Europe is almost certainly the radial-engined M4 or M4A1, but in the USA there are more

examples of the Ford-engined M4A3 and the GM diesel-engined M4A2, simply because this was the most numerous in production.

Price tends to be more dependent on condition and originality than scarcity, and as already mentioned, at the time of writing (late 2011) a well-restored, complete and running M4 will be priced in the region of £250,000, or more. The actual price will depend on the scarcity of the variant, its condition and location, and factors such as whether or not the gun is complete. For example, a Canadian-built M4A5 Grizzly was recently pulled out of long-term storage and offered for sale in Britain with a spare engine. Described as 95% complete but requiring restoration, it was priced at £125,000. A second Grizzly was offered for sale in the USA (www.armyjeeps.net), fully restored and with an 'un-cut' gun, at $375,000; remaining unsold, it was subsequently reduced to $325,000. Army Cars Germany (+49 151 53917532) recently offered for sale two complete, or near complete, Shermans, one M4 without an engine but mounting a deactivated 75mm gun, the other described as 'recovered from the battlefield, with some battle damage' but said to be restorable; the company also had a Sherman hull for sale. Finally, a duplex-drive (DD) M4A1 recovered from beneath the sea at Omaha beach, where it sank on 6 June 1944, was offered for sale from the USA, in unrestored condition, at a massive $595,000; the tank was located in France.

Restorable hulks are occasionally available, generally out of storage in the Middle East or

BELOW Surplus Sherman beach armoured recovery vehicle (BARV) seen at Pounds' Yard in Portsmouth waiting to be cut for scrap. This vehicle was subsequently rescued and restored.
(Ian Young)

ABOVE A duplex-drive M4A1, said to have been recovered from beneath the sea at Omaha Beach, was recently offered for sale in the USA in unrestored condition at a massive $595,000. Here a vehicle which was similarly recovered from the seabed is displayed at the Museum of Undersea Wrecks (*Musée des Épaves Sous-Marines du Débarquement*). *(Ian Young)*

BELOW In 1947 Robert Crawford converted this M4A4 Chrysler-engined Sherman for ploughing, firstly with the turret removed and later with the entire upper hull cut off. The machine has subsequently been restored and provides an awesome sight at enthusiasts' ploughing matches and demonstrations in the area. *(Stuart Gibbard)*

BELOW For many enthusiasts, driving around the arena at a military vehicle show will be the only opportunity for getting at the controls of a moving tank. Note the twin wading ducts fitted to this M4A4. *(Ian Young)*

ABOVE **Another privately-owned Chrysler-engined M4A4, this time seen in the main square at Béthune during the annual celebrations to commemorate the liberation of the Pas de Calais region.** *(Warehouse Collection)*

pulled from ranges, or even off a battlefield. For one of these you should expect to pay no more than perhaps £50,000, with the actual price again dependent on the scarcity of the variant and its condition.

As regards the parts that will inevitably be required for restoration, it will be necessary to fabricate some components and to trawl the Internet and military vehicle dealers stock for others. New old stock (NOS) items still come to light from time to time; and, of course, the Sherman shares some components – such as instruments, some switchgear and lighting equipment – with other World War Two American military vehicles.

However, providing your pocket can stand the initial purchase price, and always bearing in mind the adage that 'past performance is no guarantee of future results', over the past two or three decades World War Two armoured vehicles have proved to be a very canny investment. Even during the last four or five years the price of a restored Sherman has more than doubled... and, remember, they aren't making them any more!

Insurance

Whilst you might not expect that you could insure a Sherman via the Internet price-comparison websites, the process is surprisingly hassle-free, with several companies specialising in military vehicle insurance proving only too happy to take on the risk.

Regardless of whether you intend to drive on the public highway or not, it is sensible to make sure that the tank is adequately insured for all likely risks; and don't forget that insurance companies will probably refuse to honour your policy in the event of a claim if you are not correctly licensed to drive the vehicle in question. Whilst theft might appear unlikely, it is not unknown – and don't overlook the damage that a runaway tank can do. The minimum sensible cover would therefore be third-party risks, theft, fire and public liability.

Legal aspects of owning a tank

In Britain and the USA at least, there is no legislation that prevents any private individual from owning or operating a tank... but be assured that plenty of paperwork will be involved in the process of importing or exporting the thing! Other European nations may be less relaxed, and the situation in France, for example, is particularly difficult.

For would-be tank-owners based in Britain, the real difficulties arise regarding the ownership of weapons and live ammunition. The simplest, and for most people the only, practical solution is to ensure that any weapons on the tank, including the main gun, are deactivated and proof-house certified accordingly. Any tank offered for sale in Britain, be it direct from the Army or from a museum or private individual, will almost certainly have already been deactivated, and it is not possible to import a tank from overseas with its gun intact.

In the past it was, in theory, possible to gain a UK Firearm Certificate for a rifled gun,

although the authorities almost certainly did not imagine that any private individual would consider owning a fully functioning tank gun, and any application for such a Certificate might well have created some difficult discussions. In recent years the certification of firearms has been tightened up considerably, and the applicant must now show good reason for each and every weapon held on any Certificate. Further, any weapon with a calibre larger than 0.22in (5.6mm) is classified as a 'prohibited weapon' and, as such, is covered by Section 5 of the Firearms Act 1982 (as currently amended). Ownership of such a weapon requires specific authority from the Secretary of State, and it is inconceivable that such authority would be forthcoming for a 75mm or 76mm tank gun, let alone the 105mm M4 howitzer. Indeed, it is hard to see how the authorities could be convinced that there is any good reason to want to own a tank gun... but there's no harm in trying!

In the USA there are both state and federal laws controlling the ownership of guns and ammunition, with enforcement by the Bureau

BELOW Many enthusiasts like to create a diorama around their vehicles. This M4 75mm has been coated with artificial snow to form part of a Battle of the Bulge display. *(Warehouse Collection)*

of Alcohol, Tobacco, Firearms and Explosives (BATF); a tank gun is classified as a 'destructive device' by the BATF. The state laws, which vary from one state to another, are independent of existing federal law, and are sometimes broader or more limited in their scope, but in many states it is perfectly possible for a private citizen to own a live-firing tank – but inevitably, there is considerable cost and red tape involved.

Driving

To drive a Sherman (or any) tank on the public highway in Britain it is necessary to hold a 'Class H' driving licence, which covers all types of track-laying vehicles; the minimum age for driving this type of vehicle is 21. There is no restriction on driving a tank on private land, and whilst you may think that it is extremely unlikely that you might wish to drive on public roads, remember that many enthusiasts get invited to take part in parades and commemorative events, portions of which often take place on public roads, and this will require a driving licence. Many of the companies offering tank-

ABOVE Whilst theoretically possible – particularly if the Sherman in question has rubber pads on the tracks – it is not sensible to drive a tank to a military vehicle show, and some sort of transporter will be required. Nothing looks better than carrying a Sherman on the correct period tank transporter: this is the open-cabbed version of the American Diamond T Model 980/981 ballast tractor, coupled to a 40/45-ton drawbar trailer. *(Ian Young)*

BELOW Privately-owned and road-registered, this Sherman 75mm has a late pattern welded hull that lacks the direct-vision apertures for the driver and co-driver/bow machine gunner; both the driver's and the co-driver's hatches are open. The ledge running across the hull just above the number plate was fitted to help with stowing items on the glacis plate. The track is the T41 or T51 plain rubber block type. *(Simon Thomson)*

driving experience days can also arrange to provide facilities for a Class H driving test.

In the USA each state determines its own driving laws and issues licences accordingly. There are nationwide regulations and requirements for driving heavy transport vehicles commercially (for example, large trucks and buses), which include the need to hold a Commercial Driver's License, but the legislators who drew up these rules almost certainly never envisaged the use of tanks on public highways by private individuals. However, whilst a small number of states will allow a tank to be registered by a civilian for on-road use, for others it is a grey area, and a few specifically forbid it.

It is also as well to remember that, at least in Britain and Europe, if your vehicle damages the road surface – and you might be surprised at the havoc that can be wrought on soft tarmac by a skid-turning Sherman – the local authority or the highways agency will almost certainly hold you responsible for the cost of repairs.

Gaining entry to the tank

Presumably with a nod to the cavalry origins of tank crews, the procedure for actually getting into and out of the tank – which is not as straightforward as you might think – is generally

described, at least by the British Army, as 'mounting' and 'dismounting'.

No footholds, steps or handholds are provided on the hull, and access is awkward for the unpractised or less sprightly. Whilst discouraging the crew from using the sprockets or suspension as mounting points, the British Army training manual suggested that the correct way to climb onto the hull, and thus to get into the tank, was by using the lamp brackets as handholds and the mudguard, tracks, towing shackle or final-drive housing as steps. The approved method of wriggling into the hull through the hatch is with one arm by the side and the other arm lifted above the head... try it any other way and you run the risk of becoming trapped.

Exiting requires the same procedure to be followed in reverse, although squeezing out of the hatches will not be easy for the average 21st-century man!

Starting procedure

Before even considering how to start the tank, the crew is required to perform a series of checks to ensure that all mechanical systems are in good order, that the on-board equipment, including fire extinguishers, tools, etc, is present and correct, and that the track and grousers, suspension components and sprockets are not unduly worn or damaged. All of these checks may seem tedious, but remember, back in 1941 the lives of the crew might well have depended on the proper operation of the tank.

These external inspections were followed by operation of the lights and siren to ensure that they were in working order, followed by checks on the levels of the cooling water and the engine, transmission and final-drive oils. The floor of the fighting compartment was checked for water and fuel or oil leaks, and inside the engine compartment the belts for the water pumps and generator were checked for proper tension, and adjusted if necessary. The air filters were inspected to see that the oil had not thickened or risen to the 'caution' mark due to excessive ingestion of dust. Next, all four fuel valves were opened to equalise pressure in the tanks, and the fuel lines and unions checked for leaks. In view of the possibility of fire resulting from the ignition of spilled petrol in the engine compartment, it was advised that the rear doors and the engine

BELOW On the move the ride is harsh, and a Sherman will generally be noisy. Curiously, there is little sensation of power, but the tank has that seemingly unstoppable quality which makes it equally at home on or off the road or pushing its way through a building! *(Tank Museum)*

top cover should be opened, to allow the engine compartment to ventilate any fumes into the atmosphere for five minutes before the engines were started. It was also suggested that the turret hatches should be open.

The starting procedure that follows refers specifically to the Sherman M4A4, as fitted with the Chrysler A-57 multi-bank engine, since this involves the most complex series of actions, but others were basically similar – and clearly you don't want to be in a hurry to start a Sherman. Mention must also be made of the need to turn the radial engines over three times by hand to ensure that oil is cleared out of the lower cylinders; this is done by means of a large hand-crank coupled to the crankshaft via a reduction gear, making it necessary to rotate the crank by some 60 or 70 revolutions!

Inside the fighting compartment, the battery switch was now closed and the instruments checked for signs of any malfunctions, particularly the ammeter and voltmeter. With the ignition switch still in the 'off' position, the engine was cranked over for eight to ten revolutions to ensure that both the starter motor and the engine rotated freely, without any undue resistance. Then the choke can be pushed all the way forward and the hand throttle pulled out about half an inch (12mm). On the Ford-engined M4A3 it was also necessary to select the required position for the carburettor air intakes; combustion air was drawn either from the engine compartment or the fighting compartment according to the position of the air-cleaner control lever – for operation in a dusty environment it was recommended that the lever be set to draw air from inside the fighting compartment, although in winter this apparently tended to make the driver feel as though he were sitting in a cold draught.

Finally, with the ignition switch set to 'on' the starter switch could be depressed. As soon as the engine fired the choke could be partially closed and set to a point where the engine would run smoothly. At the same time, the hand throttle was set to allow the engine to run at about 1,000–1,200rpm, and the oil pressure checked on the gauge.

The engine was run for ten minutes to ensure that it was thoroughly warmed up, and then three of the fuel valves could be

LEFT You might be surprised at the havoc that can be wrought on soft tarmac by a skid-turning Sherman, and, at least in Britain and Europe, the local authority will almost certainly hold you responsible for the cost of repairs. (Tank Museum)

closed, reducing the chances of losing all of the fuel through a leak. By this time the five engine exhaust stack warning lights of the Chrysler engine should have gone out, and the temperature of the cooling system have reached around 150°F (66°C); a selector switch allowed the temperature of each of the five cylinder banks to be checked individually. And by now the choke should have been fully released.

On the move

Although considerable manual effort is required to actually operate the controls, particularly the

BELOW Remember that any breakdown that incapacitates the tank to an extent where recovery is required will be expensive and will present logistical challenges. 'Roadside' repairs are generally impossible without a very well-equipped support team. (Tank Museum)

ABOVE Some enthusiasts dream of creating their own military vehicle museum. These two Shermans (M4A3 in the foreground, M4A1E8 behind) form part of the collection of Reed Knight at Titusville, Florida. *(David Doyle)*

To the right-hand side of the driver there is a conventional gear lever allowing selection of five forward and one reverse gears. Second, third and fourth gears are arranged in a double H pattern, with first and reverse at top and bottom left, respectively; a push-button latch prevents reverse being selected inadvertently.

Although the gearbox incorporates a synchromesh mechanism, the operation of the heavy gear trains is necessarily slow, and smoother changes will be obtained by using the double de-clutching technique. The clutch is released with the engine running at about 1,000–1,100rpm, and once on the move successive gear changes are made at around 1,200rpm, 1,500rpm and 1,800rpm, representing maximum speeds in each intermediate gear of 2mph (3kmh), 3mph (5kmh), 5mph (8kmh) and 8mph (13kmh); on level terrain it is generally not necessary to use first gear. In fifth gear any of the Sherman variants is capable of a creditable 24–26mph (39–42kph) on hard surfaces, although at this speed it will consume fuel at a rate of around half a mile to the gallon (180m per litre!). It is noisy and the ride is harsh, and although there is little sensation of power in the sense that a fast car feels powerful, the tank has that seemingly unstoppable quality which makes it equally at home on or off the road or, come to that, pushing its way through a building. Cornering and road-holding abilities are irrelevant – you don't steer the machine so much as aim it, and the military training manuals warn that it is easy to get out of control on hard surfaces unless the driver has considerable experience.

steering levers, the Sherman was designed to be easy to drive and it seems that it was possible to train a driver in little more than a day or so.

As with most tracked vehicles of this period, there is no steering wheel and the driver steers the machine using a pair of levers that actuate the differential brakes. Pulling back on the left-hand lever applies the brakes to the left-hand tracks, thus turning the vehicle to the left, and vice-versa. The two levers can also be pulled back together to brake both tracks, and locked in the 'on' position to provide a parking brake. Once seated the driver is faced with three pedals, operating the accelerator, brake and clutch in the conventional manner. Controls are also provided to allow the clutch to be locked in the disengaged position; on the twin-engined M4A2 (Sherman III) there are two clutches, operated by a single pedal, but it was possible to lock out either clutch individually.

It hardly needs to be said that forward visibility is dreadful, even with the driver's hatch open... using the driver's rain hood makes visibility worse, and don't even think about driving with the hatch closed. Worse still, there is no rearward visibility to speak of at all. Obviously, the presence of a commander, in touch with the driver by radio, is essential to avoid accidents – and even at the time, training manuals suggested that the driver should take extra care to 'ensure that nothing is in the path of the tank as the vehicle moves forward'. It is also essential that all crew members wear proper safety headgear – there are a lot of sharp objects inside the hull – and that no one

RIGHT The collection of the late Jacques Littlefield at the Military Vehicle Technology Foundation in California is legendary amongst enthusiasts. The Foundation owns more than one Sherman, the exhibit shown here being an Israeli Defence Force M50 Mk 2. *(David Doyle)*

be allowed to ride on the outside of the hull, no matter how cool and 'Hollywood' it looks.

According to the manuals, reversing the tank was not to be attempted without a banksman, although this would hardly have been possible when under fire!

Stopping

The master switch should not be used to stop the engine. The correct procedure for stopping the engine is to allow it to idle for two minutes to cool down, before turning off the ignition switch, shutting off both fuel supply valves, and then turning the master switch to the 'off' position.

The tank should be left with the parking brakes properly engaged and the transmission in neutral.

Transportation

It should come as no surprise that you cannot generally drive a Sherman to a military vehicle show. If you do not own a suitable low-loader vehicle you will need to rent one, and this is not cheap. If your pockets are sufficiently deep, nothing looks better than carrying a Sherman on the correct period tank transporter.

During World War Two Shermans were moved by road using three different types of vehicle. The British Army used the Scammell Pioneer TRMU30 tractor, together with its dedicated TRCU30 semi-trailer, but with a nominal maximum load rating of 30 tons the Pioneer was pretty much at its limit with a combat-ready Sherman. In addition the Scammell was always in short supply, and from 1941 it was supplemented by the American Diamond T Model 980/981 ballast tractor, towing a 40/45-ton drawbar trailer, the latter produced by a number of British and American manufacturers with detail differences between the various models.

The US Army also used the Diamond T, although only in combination with trailers of American manufacture, describing the complete train as the 'truck-trailer, 45-ton, tank transporter, M19'; the Diamond T tractor was identified as M20. Never happy with the Hercules diesel engine of the Diamond T, which had been originally specified by the British to provide a common fuel with the Scammell Pioneer, the US Army tended to favour the M26 Pacific TR-1 'Dragon Wagon', a massive 45-ton tractor produced in both armoured and softskin configuration, and designed to be used with a Fruehauf M15 semi-trailer; in this case the train was described as 'truck-trailer, 45-ton, tank transporter, M25'.

Chapter Seven

Restoring the Sherman

Vehicle restoration is an easily described process, even if the practice is less straightforward. At its simplest it consists of little more than stripping a machine down to its constituent parts, removing rust and old paint, identifying and locating anything that is missing, and repairing or replacing any parts that are broken or sufficiently worn as to be unsuitable for further service. With this aspect of the work out of the way, the more rewarding process of reassembly can begin, with the machine generally being painted as the process continues.

OPPOSITE Over the years many Shermans have ended their lives as range targets, and although it is sometimes possible to rescue their sad remains most will be of little use beyond being a source of parts. *(Warehouse Collection)*

Despite the difficulties introduced by the size and weight of the vehicle and many of the component parts, the restoration process for a tank is essentially the same as it is for a motor car. Anyone who has restored a vintage machine of any kind will know that major problems tend to centre on the difficulty of finding parts and the extent of any corrosion or other damage to the bodywork. Whilst ownership and restoration of a Sherman will certainly not guarantee immunity from the hunt for elusive parts, since there will be plenty of little bits and pieces that have gone missing over the last 60 years, at least there will not be problems with the bodywork. Providing the tank is largely intact and has not been used as a

range target, then restoration of the hull should be relatively straightforward, albeit no small task, often needing little more than simply blast-cleaning and repainting.

Finding those elusive parts will be another problem altogether and will require cosying up to all of the dealers servicing the collectors' market as well as keeping a close eye on collectors' websites, such as www.milweb.net or www.militaryvehiclessupply.net. Nevertheless, it is surprising what still turns up: one Sherman owner recently located a brand-new Continental radial engine, still in its manufacturer's crate!

But even if parts are not missing, don't get the idea that the relatively low mileage that most tanks will have covered means that mechanical components will not be worn out. Tanks are usually required to operate in an extremely hostile environment and the constant diet of dust and other airborne filth thrown up by the tracks almost guarantees that the engines will be worn, and that the suspension and track links will have been damaged by large amounts of abrasive material. It is also common for the sprockets to be worn if the tank has covered any appreciable mileage.

Safety first

If not treated with considerable respect a tank is very liable to bite back, and bite back hard. It would be true to say that the designers didn't spend even a tea-break considering the problems likely to be faced by private owners lacking proper workshop facilities. It is equally true to say that a tank requires a lot of maintenance, if it is to be kept in fighting-fit condition – or even in running condition; and even the simplest maintenance and repair operations include the potential for all kinds of peril, some of which can result in serious personal injury. Remember that almost every component is large, awkward and very heavy.

BELOW A pair of sad M4A1s, *sans* guns, awaiting restoration. (*David Doyle*)

ABOVE Having spent some years at the bottom of the English Channel, this M4A1 DD is probably beyond salvation; the best that can be done is to maintain the vehicle in a state of arrested decay.

(Ian Young)

Personal protection

■ Before starting work, make sure that you are wearing proper mechanics' overalls and stout boots or shoes, preferably with steel toecaps. Tuck hair, neckties or other loose clothing out of harm's way. Remove rings or other jewellery to avoid the possibility of causing accidental electrical short circuits.

■ Do not even consider raising the tank using a standard commercial jack. Any jack used should be rated at 20 tons at least.

■ If you need to work inside the engine compartment with the engine running, keep your hands and fingers away from the fan and any rotating parts.

■ Remember that the exhaust system and radiator become very hot when engines are running and can cause skin burns.

■ Do not attempt to lift heavy components without adequate assistance. A good rule of thumb is to not try to lift more than 120lb (55kg) single-handedly. This figure should be reduced if the load is awkward

ABOVE View inside the fighting compartment of an unrestored Sherman that has suffered through being open to the weather.

(Ian Young)

LEFT View of the rusted turret basket and the ammunition stowage area behind the co-driver's seat.

(Ian Young)

RIGHT The more parts that are missing the harder will be the restoration. As commonly happens, this M4A4 lacks its engine and has had the gun barrel cut off. *(Ian Young)*

ABOVE It is important to have somewhere dry and secure to work – and do not underestimate the amount of space required. The tank shown is an M4A5 Grizzly. *(Warehouse Collection)*

BELOW Removing the twin engines of a GM Detroit Diesel-powered M4A2 at the Tank Museum. These engines weigh 5,110lb (2,323kg) and serious lifting equipment is required to extract the lump safely. *(Roland Groom, Tank Museum)*

or sharp-edged, or if it needs to be held at arms' length, or if you are forced into an uncomfortable working position.

■ Always wear suitable eye protection when using a grinding wheel, needle gun or powered abrasive discs, etc.

■ Do not strip paints and surface coatings without proper respiratory protection. The white paint that was originally used on the interior surfaces of the engine and fighting compartments contains lead compounds, which are potentially injurious; other old paint compounds may be similarly hazardous.

■ Be wary of any small arms or machine-gun ammunition that may be found lying in inaccessible areas of the fighting compartment; in the heat of battle no one kept track of anything that was dropped, and small rounds can easily find their way into hidden nooks and crannies.

■ Do not spray paints or other fluids without proper respiratory protection.

Potential hazards

■ Never run the engine in a closed space. Carbon monoxide exhaust gases are poisonous and can cause permanent brain damage and death.

■ Battery acid is corrosive to metal and will burn eyes, skin and clothing. Make sure it stays inside the battery!

■ The gases produced by an open-vented battery during charging and discharging are highly inflammable and can easily ignite.

■ Be careful of short-circuiting the batteries. There is sufficient voltage and current available to cause the battery casing to split, to start a fire in the wiring, or to cause serious skin burns.

■ Petrol and other fuel vapours are highly inflammable; petrol, particularly, has a flashpoint of –40°C (–40°F), which means that it is liable to ignite in any normal ambient conditions. Do not expose such vapours to a naked flame, and never introduce any flame, or any apparatus that can produce a spark, into an empty fuel tank, no matter how long you believe it has been empty.

■ Do not allow oils or greases to come into contact with the skin; old engine oil, particularly, contains carcinogenic

ABOVE In order to work on the engine it is necessary to purchase or fabricate a support of some kind. This Continental R-975 radial engine is attached to a purpose-made frame. *(Warehouse Collection)*

compounds. Wear disposable gloves or use a skin barrier cream.

- Dispose of used fluids in a responsible manner. Most local authority waste disposal sites have facilities for old oils.

Tools and working facilities

Get hold of the proper factory documentation, including an instruction book, parts list, service (shop) manual and maintenance schedule. These documents will repay you time and again in reducing frustration and wasted effort. Reproductions are readily available and are preferable for use in the workshop anyway, since they are liable to become well thumbed and greasy. Keep the originals indoors out of harm's way!

Threaded fastenings on the vehicle use either American NF (SAE National 'fine') or NC (SAE National 'coarse') thread forms, more usually rendered as UNF and UNC these days. It is always good practice to use new zinc-plated fasteners when reassembling parts after maintenance or replacement; many components are subject to very high loadings, so be sure to replace high-tensile fasteners on a like-for-like basis.

As regards tools for day-to-day maintenance, a good selection of imperial 'AF' ('across flats') spanners and sockets will be required,

ABOVE Viewed from above, it is clear that the Chrysler A-57 multi-bank engine is a large and complex piece of equipment. *(Tank Museum)*

LEFT Continental R-975 radial engine laying on the fan shroud; note that the engine is still attached to the supporting subframe. *(Ian Young)*

LEFT Brand-new Continental R-975 still in its original packing case – a rare find indeed, and one can't help feeling that it is almost a shame to unpack it! *(Warehouse Collection)*

ABOVE LEFT View down into the empty engine compartment of an M4A5 Grizzly hull. The rear of the tank is at top left of the picture. (*Warehouse Collection*)

ABOVE View of the same M4A5 Grizzly engine compartment, this time looking towards the fighting compartment. Note the propeller shaft protruding through the bulkhead. (*Warehouse Collection*)

LEFT Putting the GM Detroit Diesel engines back into the Tank Museum's M4A2. Sadly, most enthusiasts will not have access to an armoured recovery vehicle at this stage of the work! (*Roland Groom, Tank Museum*)

but bearing in mind the size of many of the components and fastenings it is as well to have a range of heavy-duty $\frac{5}{8}$in drive sockets and accessories. Other basic tools that will be required include items such as pliers, feeler gauges, screwdrivers and hammer, etc, as well as a lever- or air-operated grease gun. More specialised jobs will involve the use of a torque wrench, while serious work will require access to heavy lifting equipment (see left).

A range of special tools was produced to simplify maintenance of the tank. These include a track puller, spring compressor, adaptor for removing and replacing idler wheels, adaptor for removing and replacing suspension arm bushes and shock absorber pins, a sling for lifting the batteries, and a fixture for removing the front power train. Almost certainly none of these tools will be available and it will be necessary to improvise.

ABOVE View down into the turret of a 'barn find' M4A5 Grizzly... note how small the access hatch is! Though largely complete, the tank will still require a considerable amount of work to bring it back to running condition. *(Warehouse Collection)*

Handling heavy components

The issue of weight will be a constant problem for the private owner, and a Sherman cannot be properly maintained or repaired without proper lifting facilities, together with a crew of three or four experienced fitters. Although welded eyes are attached to the hull in strategic positions to assist in lifting operations, the sheer size and weight of the main automotive components should not be underestimated.

For example, although the engine can be easily extracted from the hull once the deck covers have been removed, these covers cannot be lifted without the use of a crane. The engine itself also requires a 3-ton (3,000kg) gantry, and needs to be lifted to a height of 140in (3,556mm) to clear the hull. The lightest of the engines is the Wright/Continental R-975 radial which, by virtue of its aluminium construction, weighs a modest 1,137lb (517kg); whilst the GM twin diesels and the Chrysler A-57 multi-bank both weigh more than 5,200lb (2,365kg). The complete transmission weighs somewhere in the order of 11,200lb (5,091kg) and can only be removed by unbolting the housing from the hull and lifting or jacking the

ABOVE Sometimes it must be hard to know where to start! *(Ian Young)*

LEFT Many Shermans were demilitarised by having their gun barrels cut off, and these scrap barrels were photographed at Pounds' Yard in Portsmouth. It is possible to reattach a cut barrel by careful welding in such a way that the repair will be virtually invisible, even though the barrel may end up slightly longer or shorter than its maker intended... of course, it will never be able to fire again! *(Ian Young)*

LEFT Although there seems to be not a scrap of paint remaining on the hull or turret of this M4A1 75mm, the metallurgical composition of the armour, and the sheer thickness of everything, means that serious rust is rarely a problem.
(Ian Young)

hull clear. The gearbox weighs just 1,350lb (611kg) and can be separated from the transmission... once the transmission has been extracted from the hull. The main gun weighs around 2,800lb (1,275kg), and even the original batteries weigh in at 180lb (82kg) each!

Stripping the vehicle

Although essentially the same, the stripping process will vary in detail depending on the particular variant, and the following text – which refers specifically to the M4A2 (Sherman III) equipped with twin GM diesel engines – should be considered simply as representative of what is involved.

Removing the engine

According to period documentation, removing the twin engines from the M4A2 involves 14 hours' work for three men, whilst its replacement involves 22 hours' work.

The first task is to turn off the master switches and to disconnect the battery cables, before removing the rear battery and disconnecting the starter motors. The hull inspection plate needs to be removed, using jacks to support its weight, as do the engine deck covers, access doors and splashguards; to enable the deck covers to be removed, the gun must be positioned at 90° to the centreline of the tank. The engine sumps and the oil tanks must be drained, and the air cleaners, radiators, fan shrouds, exhaust pipes and filter panel should be removed.

ABOVE **View of the commander's cupola showing where the vision block is missing. Although easily replaceable, new vision blocks will not necessarily be easy to find.** *(Warehouse Collection)*

RIGHT **Rusted-through air cleaner canister at the rear of an M4A1; it will almost certainly be necessary to fabricate replacements if the originals are beyond repair.** *(Warehouse Collection)*

RIGHT **Stripped to the minimum, this welded hull is being blast-cleaned to remove all traces of paint and surface rust.** *(Rex Cadman)*

Inside the fighting compartment, one man removes the cowling over the propeller shaft, disconnects the propeller shaft at the clutch end, and removes the generators, the transmission-oil cooler, the bulkhead, the bulkhead shroud that separates the engine compartment from the fighting compartment, and the clutch-operating mechanism. A sling may now be attached to the engine in such a way that the engine is lifted at an angle of 25° in order to clear the rear plate of the engine compartment. Once all of the control cables and other connections between the engine and the various accessories have been removed, the engine may be lifted clear.

Reassembly, as they say, is the reverse of dismantling.

Removing the transmission

Before the transmission can be lifted out, the tracks must be separated and lifted clear of the sprockets, and the front of the tank jacked-up until the front bogie wheel is clear of the track. Wooden packing should be inserted under the final-drive housing leaving a clearance of 1in (25mm), and then the tank should be lowered onto the packing; this should leave the front bogie wheel just touching the track and unable to rotate by hand.

The propeller shaft and the universal-joint housing and flange should be removed and the flexible pipes on the left-hand side of the gearbox disconnected, carefully noting the position of these pipes in relation to the oil cooler. The speedometer cable and the oil thermometer on the gearbox should be

disconnected and unclipped, and the clevis pins removed from the top of the steering brake rods. The shelf above the gearbox should be removed, together with its support tubes, allowing the power train oil cooler to be removed. Finally, the cross shaft for the right-hand steering brake must be removed from the top of the power train, and the stoplight switches and their brackets removed.

ABOVE **View inside a stripped hull looking towards the rear.** *(Rex Cadman)*

LEFT **Stripped hull of an M4A3E2 assault tank awaiting restoration in Utah. The M4A3E2 hull was up-armoured on all surfaces, and there was a new heavy turret mounting the 75mm M3 gun.** *(David Doyle)*

LEFT **This blast-cleaned hull has had the complete nose casting – which contains the final drive – removed, allowing a view inside the hull.** *(Rex Cadman)*

The bolts securing the power train to the hull can now be removed and, with fourth gear selected, the tank can be separated from the power train with the aid of a jack, and the hull and the transmission prised apart. Once the transmission has been separated from the tank the gearbox can be removed from the power train housing using a suitable sling.

The clutches can be removed either with the engines in situ or after the engines have been extracted.

Removing the suspension units

It is possible to remove the centre bogie assembly without breaking the track, but for other units the track on the affected side must be separated and lifted clear.

For vertical volute spring suspension, two plugs must be removed from the top of the suspension bracket and two bolts, 16.2in long and 0.8125in in diameter (412 x 20.6mm), should be inserted through the suspension bracket from below so that they protrude through the plug holes. Nuts and washers should be placed on the top of the bolt and finger-tightened. The tank can now be jacked up until the ends of the spring saddle levers are clear of the rubbing plates on the suspension arms, and the six bolts that secure the bracket caps to the bracket can be removed. The suspension arms will drop when the last bolt is removed, and your hands should be kept well clear to avoid injury. Using a ten-ton hydraulic jack and a plate placed under the spring

saddle, the saddle should be raised sufficiently to release the tension on the compressor bolts so that they can be removed; with the bolts out of the way, the jack can be slowly lowered to allow the spring to extend; the saddle and saddle spring lever will fall away and can be removed and dismantled.

The process is different for horizontal volute spring suspension. The tank should first be jacked up on the affected side by about two inches (50mm) using either one 30-ton jack or a pair of 15-ton jacks. Once the tank is raised on the jack, the shock absorber can be removed by unbolting the pinch bolts and knocking-out the pins. The tank should then be jacked higher until all of the road wheels are clear of the track by at least one inch (25mm). Both road wheels on the affected side can now be prised down so that the spring seat tilts sufficiently to allow the springs to be removed. After removing the pinch bolts, end-cap screws and end caps the wheels can be lifted off the track and the whole suspension assembly lifted clear of the support bracket.

Removing the tracks

On any tank that has been standing for a length of time, the track pins and bushes will almost certainly be seized, or partially seized. In extreme cases it will be necessary to strip and clean the entire length of track, which is a long and laborious process, but it is also possible to free off partially seized tracks by running the tank – it might be sensible to spray all of the pins with penetrating fluid before attempting this.

If the tracks need to be removed, it is first necessary to remove the sand guards, if fitted. Next the idler bracket should be slackened off by undoing the two clamp bolts, and the centre bolt on the adjustable idler bracket should be screwed in. Using the special track-adjusting spanner, the serrated locking plate should be released, and the plate tapped off the serrations

LEFT DD tanks had a crown wheel fitted behind each of the rear idlers as part of the drive system to the propellers; it will prove almost impossible to locate the missing parts. *(Ian Young)*

RIGHT Even where a tank is superficially complete it will almost certainly be necessary to replace all of the external sheet metal parts, including the lights, track guards (where fitted) and brackets, etc. Fortunately these items are either easy to fabricate or, in the case of lights, relatively easy to find. *(Warehouse Collection)*

ABOVE Here the Tank Museum's M4A2 is being towed back across one of the tracks, which has been laid out on the ground, in order to allow the track to be looped around the sprocket, return rollers and idler and the two ends linked together and tensioned. *(Roland Groom, Tank Museum)*

in order to release the idler spindle. The track can now be set to the slackest position.

With the tracks slackened off, the run should be separated between the front bogie wheel and sprocket, or between the rear bogie wheel and the idler, by removing the wedge bolts and taking off the side plates before driving out the connecting pin. If the track run is broken at the rear end the engine can be used to drive the track forward over the front sprockets, whereas if the break is made at the front the track must be manhandled over the rear idler.

To replace the tracks the above procedure is reversed, using the track jack finally to pull the two ends together before driving in the final pin to connect the two track shoes.

Removing the main gun

The first thing to be removed is the deflector guard, allowing the clamp to be slackened and the pin removed from the stabiliser piston rod. The gyro box should be disconnected at the multi-pin plug, the control cable detached from the gun-elevating gear, and the gyro box itself disconnected from its mounting bracket. The recoil switch should be removed from the gun and the cable unclipped; the firing solenoids for the two turret machine guns should be removed and the wiring unclipped. Remove the elevating

gear from the cross shaft, disconnect the link between the gun mounting and the periscope, and remove the elevating stop.

The bolts holding the mantlet to the turret can now be removed and the gun lifted free using a suitable sling.

Repairing the hull

If the hull has sustained ballistic damage that is sufficiently serious to either crack castings or open welds and distort the normally flat armour to any serious extent, then it will almost certainly be beyond economic repair. Partial penetrations caused by impact with small arms or heavy machine-gun fire can either be left alone as the honourable scars of battle, or ground flat and filled before being repainted – of course, the original strength of the armour will be compromised, but this should be of no consequence in an average suburban environment. Small penetrations that have actually passed right through the armour can be ground down, and plugged and filled with any suitable material, or even filled with weld if the penetration is small; but again, the original strength of the material will have been lost.

During World War Two, welded hulls for armoured vehicles were generally manufactured by electrode welding using heavy-gauge electrodes, sometimes up to 0.375in (9.5mm) diameter, and several runs were required to build up a joint of a given size. Clearly, heavy welding currents were involved and equipment of this type will not be available to the average restorer. However, since the ultimate strength of the weld is of less importance in restoration work it is possible to reattach welded fittings using MIG (metal, inert gas) or pulsed MIG techniques, using Type 307 stainless-steel filler rod.

Repairing the main gun

Almost any Sherman sold in Britain will have had the main gun de-militarised to ensure that it cannot be fired. This often involves welding the breech shut and cutting into, or in extreme cases cutting off, the barrel. Little can be done to recover a welded breech beyond cosmetic restoration.

A barrel that has been cut into can generally be 'repaired' by patching, welding and filling the cut areas, but of course, it will never be

RIGHT View of the restored driving compartment... what a shame that the crew need to walk all over this shiny paint in dirty boots!
(Ian Young)

fit for live firing. If the barrel has been cut off it is possible to replicate a new section using steel piping, or even wood, but it will be hard to replicate the exposed wall thickness at the muzzle end and the gentle taper which was evident along the length of the barrel itself.

BELOW Any usage at all will result in the finished product being covered with dust or mud, as this M4A4 demonstrates. *(Simon Thomson)*

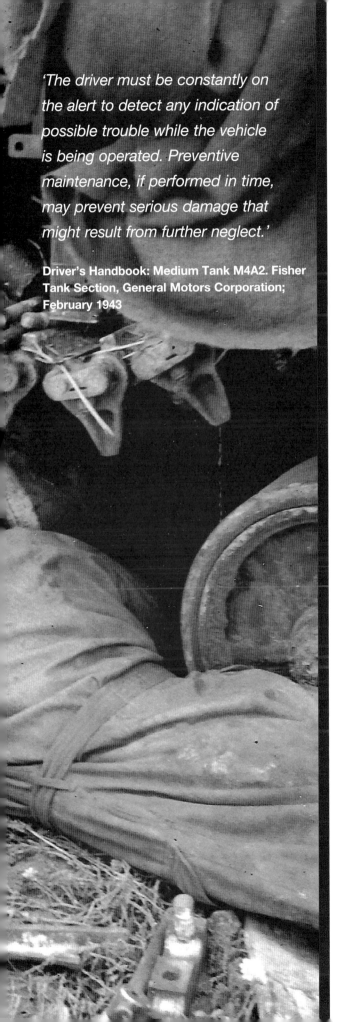

Chapter Eight

Maintaining the Sherman

Under its original operating conditions the Sherman required daily maintenance, with regular oil changes and attention from the grease gun to keep it in peak operating condition. It is unlikely that the private owner will need to follow what is an extremely rigorous schedule. Nevertheless, close attention should be paid to the manufacturer's recommendations, even if the maintenance intervals are extended to suit occasional use. It is also sensible, particularly if the timescale is extended, to keep a written record of a proper maintenance schedule.

OPPOSITE Hopefully this is not the sort of work that will need to be undertaken by the average private owner. The photograph shows the damage caused to a Sherman suspension unit that has been hit by a German 88mm shell. The tank crew, members of Westminster Dragoons, 27th Armoured Brigade, are attempting 'roadside' repairs. (IWM, B5423)

ABOVE **Access to
much of the equipment
inside the hull is
extremely difficult!**
(Simon Thomson)

Day-to-day problems and reliability issues

The Sherman was designed to provide the highest standards of mechanical reliability and to be easy to repair, particularly when compared to the complex German tanks. Features such as the volute spring suspension, rubber-bushed tracks, rear-mounted (air-cooled) engine and front drive sprockets all helped to contribute to the vehicle's mechanical reliability, and if the users expressed any criticisms of the Sherman these usually concentrated on the lack of sufficient firepower and protection rather than

on any specific problems with reliability. Most of the changes incorporated into the design during production were aimed at improving the ability of the Sherman to survive in combat and to improve its performance rather than to eliminate design weaknesses.

Nevertheless, US Ordnance personnel responsible for keeping the armies moving calculated that something like 30–40% of a column of tanks would require some sort of attention as a result of failure during a typical 40–50 mile (65–80km) day's 'march'. Such attention might range from simply changing drive belts or sparking plugs to removing

ABOVE Given the right equipment – in this case in the shape of a six-ton Kenworth M1 heavy wrecker – it is possible to change an engine in the field. The engine itself is the Wright or Continental R-975 radial. *(Tank Museum)*

RIGHT Photograph from the US Army technical manual showing how the Ford GAA engine can be extracted from the engine compartment using a purpose-made sling. *(Warehouse Collection)*

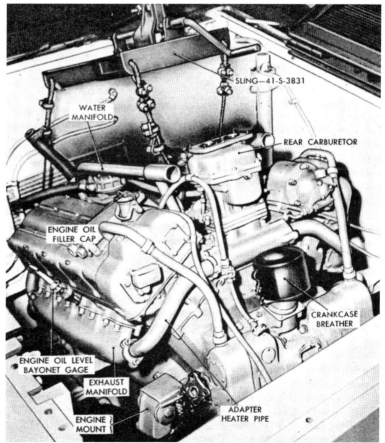

WATER MANIFOLD

SLING—41-S-3831

REAR CARBURETOR

ENGINE OIL FILLER CAP

ENGINE OIL LEVEL BAYONET GAGE

EXHAUST MANIFOLD

ENGINE MOUNT

CRANKCASE BREATHER

ADAPTER HEATER PIPE

and replacing a suspension unit or even the complete transmission. And it was still the practice of these maintenance crews to pull the engines out after 100 hours' operation to inspect them thoroughly.

The Ford-engined M4A3 was considered to be the most reliable variant, particularly when combined with the wide-track horizontal volute spring suspension system. On the other side of the coin, the Chrysler multi-bank engined M4A4 quickly acquired a reputation for being temperamental, and ideally needed to be removed from the hull to allow access to its various components and accessories. The Wright

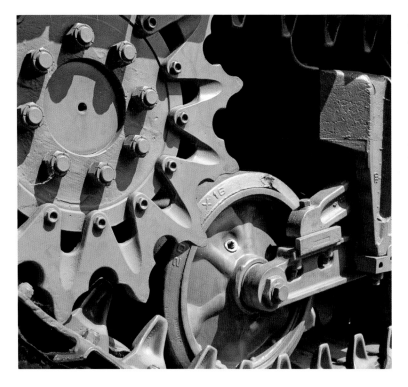

ABOVE **The condition
of the teeth on the
drive sprockets is
very important; a
sprocket that is not
worn excessively can
be reversed to present
the opposing face of
the teeth to the tracks.**
(Warehouse Collection)

RIGHT **There are
plenty of nipples
(zerks) requiring
regular attention from
the grease gun; this is
the nipple on one of
the track return rollers.**
(Warehouse Collection)

FAR RIGHT **Worn
track link connectors
should be replaced.**
(Warehouse Collection)

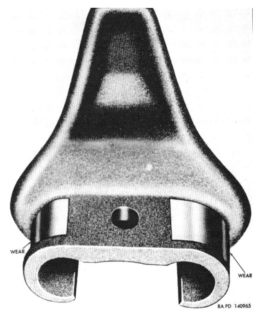

was so cold that tank tracks sometimes became frozen into the ground.

Documentation produced by the Royal Electrical and Mechanical Engineers in 1951, recounting the Corps' wartime experiences, included a breakdown of components that had created maintenance problems during the months following the D-Day landings. The Wright and Continental radial engines had a very short life (about 1,000 miles, or 1,600km) before bore and piston wear started to create problems with oiling-up; these engines were also very prone to oil leaks, and hydrostatic lock – caused by oil draining into the lower cylinders – resulted in more than a few casualties. The twin GM diesels were prone to air cleaner problems, and there were difficulties with the operation of the twin clutches.

The transmission was largely trouble-free, although the synchromesh mechanism wore quickly; such breakdowns as occurred were often due to shearing of the final-drive sprocket bolts as a result of all of the torque being applied to the bolts themselves, stress fractures of the final drive shafts due to excessive shock loading, and breakage of the propeller shaft as a result of excessive revolutions when descending a hill. Finally, the power traverse pinions on the turret frequently sheared due to the gun barrel encountering an obstruction; the lack of a friction clutch meant that any shock loading caused failure at the weakest point.

and Continental air-cooled radial engines were similarly difficult to access and were prone to fouling the plugs at idle speed. And don't forget, the problems with accessing components buried in the depths of the engine compartment were exacerbated during the winter months when maintenance crews were wearing gloves – the winter weather was a particular problem during the Ardennes Offensive (the Battle of the Bulge) in December 1944 and January 1945, when it

If the tank is to be driven at any speed on hard surfaces it is as well to remember that the tracks will have a finite life, as will the drive sprockets, regardless of whether rubber or steel track shoes are fitted. Worn track shoe connectors should be replaced to prevent damage to the sprockets, and if the rear idler wheels are out of line the tank will tend to pull to one side. Steel tracks will also destroy the surface of the road – when Chrysler switched to fitting steel tracks in 1942 the company's concrete test track was destroyed in little more than three months, with some 4.5in (115mm) of thickness worn away on the curves!

It is unlikely that any private owner will be covering high mileages, and thus is unlikely to encounter the types of failure experienced when operating a tank under combat conditions. Nevertheless, do not underestimate the inconvenience of any kind of mechanical failure; even a task that would appear to be relatively simple, such as replacing the batteries, requires a sling and a crane, and access to most components is awkward to say the least.

Lubrication

The original maintenance schedule is extremely onerous, and itemises the following tasks (based on Ford-engined M4A3 variant), with gun-related maintenance tasks excluded:

Daily operations
- Cooling water, engine and air-filter oil levels should be checked.
- Handle on oil filter should be turned daily to ensure proper operation.

Weekly operations
- The turret supporting bearing should be greased using NLGI grease number 1; the turret should be traversed during the operation.
- The turret traversing ring and pinion gear and the turret ring box adaptor should be greased using NLGI grease number 1.
- The oil level in the accessory driveshaft housing should be checked and, if necessary, topped-up with engine oil (see lubrication chart on page 150).

ABOVE Access to the final drive is available only by removing the complete nose of the tank and lifting or jacking the hull clear; the total weight of this assembly is 11,200lb (5,091kg). Workers on the 'final drive department' at Detroit Tank Arsenal had purpose-designed dollies to allow the transmission to be rolled into position before being bolted in place. *(Warehouse Collection)*

- The oil level in the transmission, differential and final-drive housing should be checked and, if necessary, topped-up with engine oil (see lubrication chart on page 150).

Monthly operations
- The traversing-gear shaft bearing, the traversing gearbox and the azimuth indicator shaft should be greased using NLGI grease number 1.

Six-monthly operations
- The transmission, differential and final-drive housing oil should be drained and refilled. Original oil grade was SAE 50 in temperatures above 32°F (0°C), SAE 30 in temperatures between 40°F (4.5°C) and –10°F (–23°C), and SAE 5 in temperatures between 0°F (–17°C) and –65°F (–53°C). Be

warned, the oil capacity for a full drain and refill is around 33 imperial gallons (40 US gallons, 150 litres).

Every 250 miles (400km)

■ The crankcase breather, the air cleaner to the auxiliary generator and the breathers in the driver's compartment should be cleaned.

■ The air filters should be drained and refilled using engine oil (see below).

Every 1,000 miles (1,600km)

■ Engine oil should be drained and refilled. Original oil grade was SAE 50 in temperatures above 32°F (0°C), SAE 30 in temperatures between 40°F (4.5°C) and

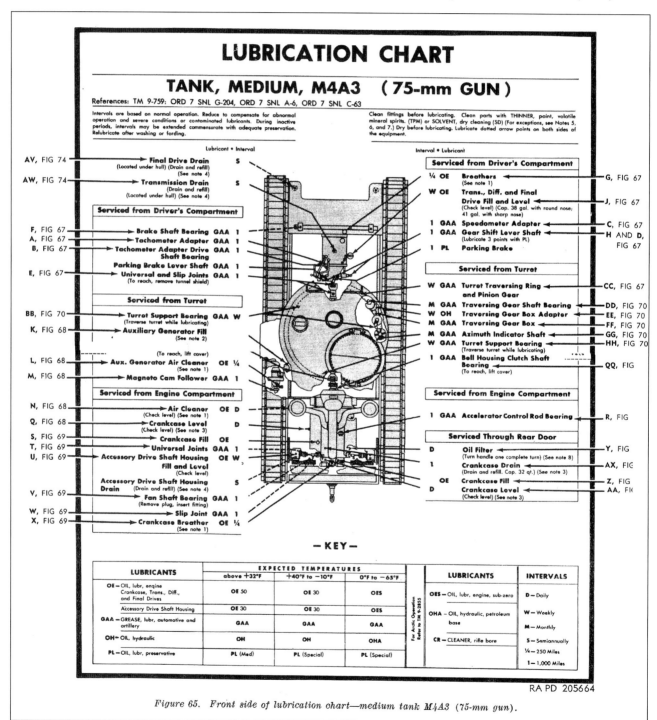

Figure 65. Front side of lubrication chart—medium tank M4A3 (75-mm gun).

−10°F (−23°C), and SAE 5 in temperatures between 0°F (−17°C) and −65°F (−53°C).

■ The transmission, differential and final-drive housing oil should be drained and refilled. Original oil grade was SAE 50 in temperatures above 32°F (0°C), SAE 30 in temperatures between 40°F (4.5°C) and −10°F (−23°C), and SAE 5 in temperatures between 0°F (−17°C) and −65°F (−53°C).

■ NLGI grease number 1 should be applied to the brake-shaft bearing, tachometer adaptor and drive gear, parking-brake lever shaft, parking brake, propeller-shaft universal and slip joints, magneto cam follower, fan-shaft bearing, speedometer adaptor, gear-shift lever shaft, clutch-shaft bearing, and the accelerator control shaft bearing.

Always make sure that you are using the correct lubricant for the job... do not assume that modern synthetic oils will necessarily be an improvement. The engine does not generate the same temperatures and stresses as a modern engine and was designed to run on a straight mineral engine oil; the most appropriate modern oil for use in temperate climates is probably a high-quality 20W-50 multigrade.

ABOVE More suspension damage, again almost certainly the result of running over a mine. Notice how one of the road wheels is completely destroyed. *(Warehouse Collection)*

Table 12: Capacities

Engine sump, drain and refill	M4, M4A1, M4A5, 7.5gal (9 US gal, 34 litres). M4A2, 5.85gal (7 US gal, 26.5 litres). M4A3, M4A4, 6.67gall (8 US gal, 30.25 litres). M4A6, 13 gal (15.5 US gal, 58.5 litres).
Transmission and differential	31.5–33gal (38–40 US gal, 144–151 litres), according to nose construction.
Air filters	0.36gal (0.45 US gal, 1.67 litres) each.
Radiator and cooling system	Approximately 11.5gal (14 US gal, or 53 litres), according to variant.
Fuel tanks	123–145gal (148–175 US gal, 560–662 litres), according to variant.

Epilogue

Almost 50,000 Shermans were built between 1942 and 1945. Many were lost in combat, and many tank crew died fighting for freedom during the darkest years of human history. The Sherman remained in service with the Allies into the post-war period, with many eventually passing into the hands of developing nations – before small numbers started to find surprising new owners. Few could have imagined that private individuals would be in a position to own a tank, much less actually *want* to do so. Yet dozens of Shermans have been restored to running order, and the vehicle is highly-prized by vintage military vehicle aficionados.

OPPOSITE Twenty five years ago private ownership of tanks would have been regarded with some suspicion, and yet today there are said to be more tanks in private hands in Britain than are operated by the British Army. Whilst this is almost certainly not the case in the USA, there is, nevertheless, no shortage of privately-owned armour – here we see Kevin and Thea Kronlund's M4A3 in operation at their 'open house' event in 2009. *(David Doyle)*

Appendices

Table 13: Typical dimensions and weights

Variant:	M4		M4A1		M4A2		
	75mm	105mm	75mm	76mm	75mm	76mm	
Dimensions							
Length, overall	232in (5,893mm)	244in (6,198mm)	230in (5,842mm)	294in (7,468mm)	233in (5,918mm)	298mm (7,569mm)	
Length, without gun	232in (5,893mm)	244in (6,198mm)	230in (5,842mm)	244in (6,198mm)	233in (5,918mm)	248mm (6,300mm)	
Width	103in (2,616mm)	103in (2,616mm)	103in (2,616mm)	103in (2,616mm)	103in (2,616mm)	103in (2,616mm)	
Height over turret	108in (2,743mm)	116in (2,946mm)	108in (2,743mm)	117in (2,972mm)	108in (2,743mm)	117in (2,972mm)	
Track centres	83in (2,108mm)	83in (2,108mm)	83in (2,108mm)	83in (2,108mm)	83in (2,108mm)	83in (2,108mm)	
Ground clearance	17in (432mm)	17in (432mm)	17in (432mm)	17in (432mm)	17in (432mm)	17in (432mm)	
Weight							
Un-stowed	62,800lb (28,545kg)	62,800lb (28,545kg)	62,700lb (28,500kg)	64,600lb (29,364kg)	66,000lb (30,000kg)	67,300lb (30,590kg)	
Combat weight	66,900lb (30,410kg)	69,400lb (31,545kg)	66,800lb (30,364kg)	70,600lb (32,091kg)	70,200lb (31,909kg)	73,400lb (33,364kg)	
Ground pressure	13.7lbf/in^2 (0.96kgf/cm^2)	14.3lbf/in^2 (1.0kgf/cm^2)	13.7lbf/in^2 (0.96kgf/cm^2)	14.5lbf/in^2 (1.0kgf/cm^2)	14.4lbf/in^2 (1.0kgf/cm^2)	15.1lbf/in^2 (1.1kgf/cm^2)	
Performance							
Maximum road speed	24mph (39kmh)	24mph (39kmh)	24mph (39kmh)	24mph (39kmh)	30mph (49kmh)	30mph (49kmh)	
Range	120 miles 195km	100 miles (162km)	120 miles (195km)	100 miles (162km)	150 miles (243km)	100 miles (162km)	
Maximum incline	1:16	1:16	1:16	1:16	1:16	1:16	
Trench crossing	89in (2,260mm)	89in (2,260mm)	89in (2,260mm)	89in (2,260mm)	89in (2,260mm)	89in (2,260mm)	
Vertical climb	24in (610mm)	24in (610mm)	24in (610mm)	24in (610mm)	24in (610mm)	24in (610mm)	
Minimum turning circle	62ft (18.91m)	62ft (18.91m)	62ft (18.91m)	62ft (18.91m)	62ft (18.91m)	62ft (18.91m)	
Fording depth	40in (1,016mm)	40in (1,016mm)	40in (1,106mm)	40in (1,016mm)	40in (1,016mm)	40in (1,016mm)	

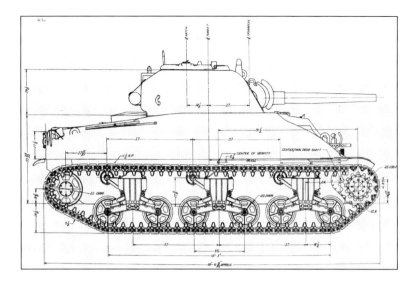

M4A3 (HVSS)			M4A3E2	M4A4	M4A5	M4A6
75mm	76mm	105mm	75mm	75mm	75mm	75mm
233in (5,918mm)	297in (7,544mm)	247in (6,274mm)	247in (6,274mm)	239in (6,071mm)	230in (5,842mm)	239in (6,071mm)
233in (5,918mm)	247mm (6,274mm)	247in (6,274mm)	247in (6,274in)	239in (6,071mm)	230in (5,842mm)	239in (6,071mm)
118in (2,997mm)	118in (2,997mm)	118in (2,997mm)	116in (2,946mm)	103in (2,616mm)	103in (2,616mm)	103in (2,616mm)
108in (2,743mm)	117in (2,972mm)	116in (2,946mm)	116in (2,946mm)	108in (2,743mm)	108in (2,743mm)	108in (2,743mm)
89in (2,261mm)	89in (2,261mm)	89in (2,261mm)	83in (2,108mm)	83in (2,108mm)	83in (2,108mm)	83in (2,108mm)
17in (432mm)	17in (432mm)	17in (432mm)	17in (432mm)	16in (406mm)	17in (432mm)	16in (406mm)
62,500lb (28,410kg)	68,100lb (30,955kg)	66,400lb (30,182kg)	77,500lb (35,227kg)	65,400lb (29,727kg)	62,700lb (28,500kg)	65,800lb (29,909kg)
66,700lb (30,318kg)	74,200lb (33,727kg)	72,900lb (33,136kg)	84,000lb (38,182kg)	69,700lb (31,682kg)	66,800lb (30,364kg)	70,000lb (31,818kg)
11lbf/in^2 (0.77kgf/cm^2)	11lbf/in^2 (0.77kgf/cm^2)	10.8lbf/in^2 (0.76kgf/cm^2)	14.5lbf/in^2 (1.0kgf/cm^2)	13.2lbf/in^2 (0.93kgf/cm^2)	13.7lbf/in^2 (0.96kgf/cm^2)	13.2lbf/in^2 (0.93kgf/cm^2)
26mph (42kmh)	26mph (42kmh)	26mph (42kmh)	22mph (36kmh)	25mph (40kmh)	24mph (39kmh)	30mph (49kmh)
130 miles (211km)	100 miles (162km)	100 miles (162km)	100 miles (162km)	100 miles (162km)	120 miles (195km)	120 miles (195km)
1:16	1:16	1:16	1:16	1:16	1:16	1:16
89in (2,260mm)	89in (2,260mm)	89in (2,260mm)	89in (2,260mm)	96in (2,438mm)	89in (2,260mm)	96in (2,438mm)
24in (610mm)	24in (610mm)	24in (610mm)	24in (610mm)	24in (610mm)	24in (610mm)	24in (610mm)
62ft (18.91m)	62ft (18.91m)	62ft (18.91m)	74ft (22.57m)	70ft (21.35m)	62ft (18.91m)	70ft (21.35m)
36in (915mm)	36in (915mm)	36in (915mm)	36in (915mm)	42in (1,067mm)	40in (1,016mm)	42in (1,067mm)

Table 14: Manufacturing contracts, serial numbers and US Army registration numbers, 1941–45

This table includes all available data, but is not necessarily comprehensive.

Manufacturer	Contract number	Year(s)	US Army registration numbers	Serial numbers
M4 variants				
American Locomotive	W-ORD-485	1941	USA 3033885–3034254	4124–4473
			USA 3066484–3066983	4305–4804
			USA 3033235–3034234	24705–25704
			USA 3072902–3073201	40305–40604
Baldwin Locomotive	W-ORD-1814	1941	n/a	1917–2304
			USA 3022537–3023381	15435–16279
Chrysler Corporation (DATP)	W-ORD-461	1943–44	USA 3032037–3032434	60174–60571
			USA 3098789–3099486	4255–43252
			USA 30100462–30101041	44228–44807
			USA 30103603–30104302	56921–57620
			USA 30111769–30112183	58208–58622
			USA 30120071–30120196	64132–64257
			USA 30139426–30139825	73436–73835
Lima Locomotive	W-ORD-694	1942	USA 3058972–3059071	25705–25804
			USA 3067630–3067901	25805–26076
Pressed Steel	W-ORD-717	1942	n/a	32104–32204
			USA 3015661–3015983	10660–10982
			USA 3036535–3036760	28005–28230
Pullman-Standard	W-ORD-718	1942–43	USA 3088017–3088242	6205–6430
			USA 3039872–3040334	30205–30667

BELOW A Normandy monument – this M4A1 76mm with HVSS suspension stands near Utah Beach, where the US Army 4th and 90th Infantry Divisions landed on D-Day. *(Ian Young)*

BELOW With a patina of light rust and with little trace of its original paint, this M4A4 stands outside the *Musée Memorial d'Omaha Beach*. *(Warehouse Collection)*

Manufacturer	Contract number	Year(s)	US Army registration numbers	Serial numbers
M4A1 variants				
Lima Locomotive	W-ORD-1159	1942	USA 3058317–3058971	6805–7459
			USA 3038135–3038734	29605–30204
Pacific Car & Foundry	W-ORD-2557	1942	USA 3060572–3061372	3005–3804
			USA 3061373–3061497	13460–13584
Pressed Steel	W-ORD-717	1941–45	USA 3014761–3015660	5–904
			USA 3015984–3016460	10983–11459
			USA 3036761–3038134	28231–29604
			USA 3069497–3070496	36900–37899
			n/a	31805–32103
			USA 30133706–30135085	69874–71253
			USA 3084447–3085277	51850–52680
			USA 3070497–3071626	37900–39029
			USA 30125680–30127006	67701–69027
			USA 30135486–30135598	71654–71766
			USA 30140226–30140435	73856–74045
M4A2 variants				
American Locomotive	W-ORD-485	1941	USA 3033735–3033884	4474–4623
Baldwin Locomotive	W-ORD-1814	1942	n/a	1905–1916
Federal Machine & Welder	W-ORD-1261	1942	USA 3055965–3056504	14785–15324
Fisher Tank Grand Blanc	W-ORD-1241	1941–45	USA 3014311–3014359	2305–2353
			USA 3020861–3021161	2354–2654
			USA 3062709–3064708	7460–9459
			USA 3064709–3064983	16280–16554
			USA 3034835–3036486	26305–27956
			USA 3036499–3036534	27969–28004
			USA 3080152–3080440	47555–47843
			USA 3080441–3081211	47844–48614
			USA 30116407–30116801	63385–64779
			USA 30116802–30117019	63780–63997
			USA 30122237–30123236	64258–65257
			USA 30129507–30130352	69028–69873
			USA 30135599–30136448	71767–72616
Pressed Steel	W-ORD-717	1944–45	USA 30142759–30142908	76074–76223
Pullman-Standard	W-ORD-718	1941–42	USA 3053115–3053614	905–1404
			USA 3095651–3096850	9460–10659
			USA 3038735–3039371	30668–31304
			USA 3096851–3097250	13585–13984
M4A3 variants				
Chrysler Corporation (DATP)	W-ORD-461	1943–45	USA 30111184–30111768	57623–58207
			USA 30103303–30103602	56621–56920
			USA 30120197–30120328	64000–64131
			USA 30124580–30125035	65258–65713
			USA 30136724–30137267	72892–73435
			USA 30140436–30142463	74046–76073
Fisher Grand Blanc	W-ORD-1241	1943–45	USA 30115882–30116406	62860–63384
			USA 30123237–30123436	67501–67700
			USA 30136599–30136723	72767–72891
			USA 3082923–3083176	50326–50579
Ford Motor Company	W-ORD-1213	1941–42	USA 3055615–3055964	2655–3004
			USA 3053615–3054954	11460–12799
M4A4 variants				
Chrysler Corporation (DATP)	W-ORD-461	1941	USA 3056615–3058014	4805–6204
			USA 3016861–3020860	16555–20554
			USA 3029082–3031158	20555–22631
			USA 3031162–3031182	22632–22652
M4A6 variants				
Chrysler Corporation (DATP)	W-ORD-461	1943	USA 3099687–3099761	43453–43527

Parts availability

The M4 Sherman was one of the most numerous armoured vehicles of World War Two, with correspondingly large volumes of spare parts manufactured and shipped around the world. During the years following the end of the war, huge amounts of this materiel was disposed of simply for its scrap value, whilst many parts were passed to those European and Middle Eastern armies that had purchased, or been gifted, tanks. As time went on and the Sherman passed further down the food chain, more and more parts were disposed of, and since at the time, there was no interest in such materiel beyond its scrap value, little seems to have survived beyond those parts that are shared with other more practical or widely-traded vehicles. It may well be that there are mountains of Sherman parts still carefully stored away in some ordnance depot in India, Iran, Israel, or Pakistan, but such materiel is not likely to appear on the Western collectors' market.

Although most parts certainly exist, the search for any specific item is liable to be fairly laborious and the best course of action is probably to approach an established dealer in ex-military hardware who may have contacts that can help.

Museums may be in a position to trade parts or to sell surplus items, and range targets can sometimes provide a useful source of parts, or at least patterns for parts, providing permission can be obtained to enter the range and remove items from the wreck. At the time of writing it is not known whether there are any Sherman hulks remaining on British ranges, but not so many years ago one British military vehicle dealer located two or three Chrysler multi-bank engines that were being used as targets and 'saved' them for parts. For details on ranges in Britain, contact the Ministry of Defence via www.mod.uk, but don't expect them to be able to tell you where there might be a Sherman.

Documentation

Like all military vehicles, the Sherman is the subject of an extraordinarily large volume of official paperwork covering every aspect of its operation, maintenance and repair. Tracking down copies of these items is not as difficult as might be imagined, and many enthusiasts actually seek out and collect official documents, manuals, photographs and other literature relating to their chosen vehicle.

Some of the major official technical manuals produced for the US Army are listed below.

Gun tanks

- TM 9-731A. Tank, medium, M4 and M4A1, 75mm gun. December 1943.
- TM 9-731AA. Tank, medium, M4 and M4A1, 76mm gun, 105mm howitzer. June 1944.
- TM 9-731B. Tank, medium, M4A2, 75mm gun. January 1943.
- TM 9-759, Tank, medium, M4A3, M4A3(W), 75mm gun, 76mm gun, 105mm howitzer. September 1944.
- TM 9-7018, Tank, medium, M4A3, M4A3(W),

BELOW LEFT Post-war edition of the US Army technical manual TM9-7018, covering all versions of the Ford-engined M4A3. *(Warehouse Collection)*

CENTRE British Army training document covering the diesel-engined M4A2 (Sherman III). *(Warehouse Collection)*

FAR RIGHT British Army training document describing the 75mm M3 gun, regardless of the tank into which it has been fitted. *(Warehouse Collection)*

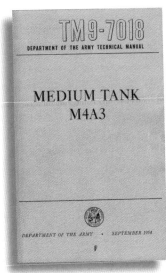

75mm gun, 76mm gun, 105mm howitzer.
September 1954.
- TM 9-754, Tank, medium, M4A4, 75mm gun. January 1943.
- TM 9-756, Tank, medium, M4A6, 75mm gun. December 1943.

Armoured recovery vehicles

- TM 9-738. Vehicle, tank recovery, M32, M32B1, M72B2, M32B3, M32B4. December 1943.

Engines

- TM 9-1730C. Engine, Wright Whirlwind R975-EC-2.
- TM 9-1731B. Engine, Ford GAA, GAF, GAN.
- TM 9-1750. Power train unit for medium tanks M3, M4 and modifications.
- TM 9-1750G. Engine, GM twin diesel 6-71.
- TM 9-1750K. Tracks and suspension, turret and hull for medium tanks M4 and modifications.
- TM 9-1751. Engine, Wright Whirlwind R975EC-2.
- TM 9-1756A. Ordnance engine, model RD-1820 (Caterpillar).

In addition each nation that operated Shermans will almost certainly have generated its own documentation. British-produced items include the following:

- AFVP/CD&M/29. Sherman II. Crew duty card.
- AFVP/G1/I. Sherman tanks (armament): all marks equipped with 75mm M3 gun.
- AFVP/VP/3. Sherman III. Vehicle training pamphlet.
- Army book 413. Sherman I and II. Crew maintenance. 1944.
- Chilwell catalogue no 72/251. Sherman V (Med M4A4): preliminary driving and maintenance instructions.
- Chilwell publication no 62/860. Repair in the field. Guide for the removal and replacement of assemblies in Sherman III tank. 1945.
- Driver's handbook. Medium tank M4A2 and 3-inch gun motor carriage M10. February 1943.

Other publications

The Sherman has always been a popular subject for military vehicle historians and there is no shortage of additional reading material available. For the serious student of the Sherman, the following small selection of titles will be found to provide useful information:

Steven Zaloga, *Armored Thunderbolt: the US Army Sherman in World War II* (Stackpole Books, Mechanicsburg, Pennsylvania, 2008, ISBN 978-0-8117-0424-3).

Gavin Birch, *Images of War: Sherman Tank* (Pen & Sword Military, Barnsley, South Yorkshire, 2005, reprinted 2007, ISBN 1-84415-187-5).

David Fletcher, *Sherman Firefly* (Osprey Publishing, Botley, Oxford, 2008, ISBN 978-1-84603-277-6).

R.P. Hunnicutt, *Sherman. A History of the American Medium Tank* (Presidio Press, Novato, California, 1978, ISBN 0-89141-080-5).

Rob Ervin and David Doyle, *WWII US Sherman Tank in Action* (Squadron Signal Publications, Carrollton, Texas, 2011, ISBN 978-0-8974-7630-0).

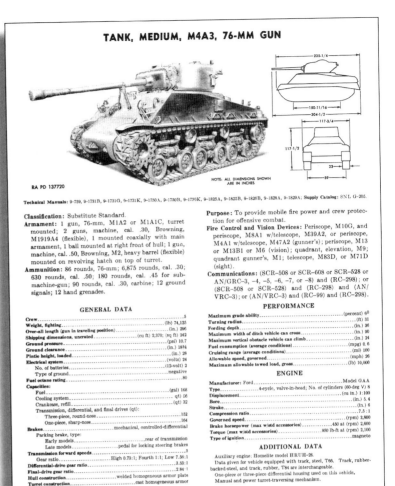

ABOVE US Army post-war (1953) specification sheet covering the M4A3 76mm; these tanks remained in US service into the mid-1950s, serving alongside the M26 Pershing and M46 Patton. *(Warehouse Collection)*

RIGHT Careful rubbing
down of the paintwork
may reveal evidence
of the original service
registration number.
(Warehouse Collection)

Service history

In theory the service records for all US Army armoured vehicles are destroyed once the vehicle is declared as surplus, although if the vehicle has come straight from a US military museum then the records may still exist, since the vehicle remained the property of Uncle Sam until disposed of. Similarly, no records have survived for those US tanks that saw service with the British Army, and the lack of any official records will make it almost impossible to discover which unit operated a particular Sherman unless genuine markings remain on the paintwork. Even if nothing is visible, it is sometimes possible to reveal earlier markings by carefully rubbing down the paint, virtually layer by layer, in the areas where markings are known to have been applied in the past. However, after almost 70 years it is very unlikely that any surviving Sherman will not have been rebuilt at least once during its military career, which may have involved service with more than one army, and perhaps once more in the hands of a museum or collector. During this process it will almost certainly have lost its integrity.

As regards other physical evidence, there may be rebuild plates on the vehicle, or on the engine or transmission, that will give some clue as to its origins and its dates in service.

If you are really lucky you may be able to find a photograph of your Sherman in service, but don't count on it.

Useful contacts

Internet

The best website for Sherman-related information is the Sherman Register (www.inter. nl.net/users/spoelstra/g104/). It is also worth checking out www.steelsoldiers.co, and www. hmvf.co.uk, which, although broader based, frequently cover tank-related topics.

Shermans in museums

There are plenty of Shermans in museums around the world. Indeed, almost any military museum of any size appears to have a Sherman exhibit.

The Tank Museum at Bovington in Dorset (www.tankmuseum.org) still has 'Michael', the oldest known Sherman to survive. It was the second Sherman off the production line at Lima Locomotive Works and was the first to be supplied to Britain under the Lend-Lease arrangements. Originally assigned the War Office registration number T25190, it was subsequently renumbered T74195, and had the early 75mm M2 gun replaced by the longer-barrelled M3 design. The Museum also has large numbers of photographs and original documentation. There are also Shermans at the Muckleburgh Collection in North Norfolk (www. muckleburgh.co.uk), the IWM Duxford (duxford. iwm.org.uk), and at the D-Day Museum at Portsmouth (www.ddaymuseum.co.uk).

As you would expect, the US Army Ordnance Museum at Aberdeen Proving Ground, Maryland, includes at least one Sherman in its collection, although at the time of writing the Museum is in the process of relocating to Fort Lee in Virginia; visit www. ordmusfound.org for the latest information. Also in Virginia, the Museum of the American Armored Foundation Inc at Danville has an M4A3E8 that was recovered after being buried for 21 years at Central Islip Psychiatric Center (www.aaftankmuseum.com). The Patton Museum of Armor and Cavalry near Fort Knox, Kentucky, has an impressive vehicle and document collection.

In France, the Museum of Undersea Wrecks (Musée des Épaves Sous-Marine du Débarquement) on the road between Bayeux and Port-en-Bessin is well worth a visit, since the exhibits have all been recovered from the seabed in the area of the D-Day landing beaches and are in what might be described as 'original, distressed condition'; telephone +33 02 31 21 17 06. There are plenty of other Shermans on show at the numerous museums

RIGHT There are Sherman monuments dotted all over Normandy, in this case an M4A2 of the Free French. *(Ian Young)*

devoted to the story of the D-Day landings and the Battle for Normandy, and the Tank Museum at Saumur is well worth a visit (www.museedesblindes.fr).

Aside from those vehicles that can be found in Britain, the USA, France, Belgium and the Netherlands there are also Shermans on display in Australia (RAAC Tank Museum, Puckapunyal, www.armytankmuseum.com. au); Canada (Canadian War Museum, Ottawa, www.warmuseum.ca); Israel (IDF Armor Corps Museum, Latrun); South Africa (School of Armour Museum, Tempe, Bloemfontein, www. saarmourmuseum.co.za); and Russia (Tank Museum, Kubinka, www.tankmuseum.ru).

BELOW All of the fascinating exhibits at the Museum of Undersea Wrecks (*Musée des Épaves Sous-Marines du Débarquement*), on the road between Port-en-Bessin and Bayeux, have been recovered from the seabed. The photograph shows a 'dozer-equipped Sherman with the 75mm gun. *(Warehouse Collection)*

ABOVE M10 tank destroyer outside the Museum of the Battle of Normandy at Bayeux. The M10 mounted a 3in anti-tank gun and was constructed using lower hulls of the M4A2 and M4A3 with a new upper hull and turret. *(Warehouse Collection)*

RIGHT Rear three-quarter view of the M4A1 that forms one of the external exhibits at the Museum of the Battle of Normandy. Note how both of the *appliqué* armour panels protecting the ammunition stowage areas have been extended at their top edges. *(Warehouse Collection)*

Military vehicle dealers and sources for parts

Although World War Two surplus continues to surface in the most unlikely places, it will certainly not be easy to find Sherman-specific parts. There is no dealer specialising in the Sherman and no one is making pattern parts. The following companies may be able to provide some assistance either with parts or restoration services, and of course it is always worthwhile keeping an eye on eBay (www.ebay.com) using the search term 'Sherman' under the category 'all of eBay motors':

Belgium

Chris Muys
J. De Blockstraat 62-A
B-2830
Tisselt
Tel (+32) 03 8867600
Website www.milweb.net/go/chrismuys/

Rietveld Auto Parts
Strichtstraat 2
9660 Michelbeke
Tel (+32) 05 5420245
Website www.milweb.net/go/rietveld

Britain

A+S
Unit 24 Roudham Park Industrial Estate
East Harling
Norfolk NR16 2QN
Tel 01953 714958
Website www.arm-soft.com

C&C Military Services
2 Lilac Cottages
High Street
Ludgershall
Buckinghamshire HP18 9PD
Tel 01296 658761

Dallas Auto Parts
Cold Ash Farm
Long Lane
Hermitage
Berkshire RG18 9LT
Tel 01635 201124
Website www.dallasautoparts.com

Robert Fleming Associates
Falcon House, Leverton Road
Sturton-le-Steeple
Retford DN22 9HE
Tel 01427 880584
Website www.bobfleming.co.uk

RR Motor Services
Sandy Lane
Great Chart
Ashford
Kent TN26 1JN
Tel 01233 820219
Website www.rrservices.co.uk

Netherlands

H.O. Wildenberg
Remmerden 44
3910 AB Rhenen
Tel (+31) 0317 61 8218
Website www.wildenbergparts.com

Stamen International Trading
Transportweg 4
7442 CT
Nijverdal
Tel (+31) 0548 61 0432
Website www.stamantechniek.nl

USA

Brent Mullins Jeep Parts (*also trading as* Army Tank Guy)
PO Box 9599
College Station
Texas 77842
Tel (+1) 979 690 0203
Website www.mullinsjeepparts.com

David M. Yamulla Jr
980 North Laurel Street
Hazleton
Pennsylvania 18201
Tel (+1) 570 454 5674
Website www.militaryvehiclesupply.net

David W. Uhrig
PO Box 726-A
Chillicothe
Ohio 45601
Tel (+1) 740 772 1540
Website www.armyjeeps.net

Northeast Military Vehicle Services
Shrewsbury
Maine 01545
Tel (+1) 800 983 0152
Website www.ww2mv.com

Sam Winer Motors Inc
3417 East Waterloo Road
PO Box 6258
Akron
Ohio 44312
Tel (+1) 330 628 4881
Website www.samwinermotors.com

TM9 Ordnance Products
256 Eagleview Boulevard, Suite 43
Exton
Pennsylvania 19341
Website www.tm9ordnance.com

Index